2nd edition
Fully revised
and extended

Understanding and Responding to Autism: The SPELL framework

A self-study guide for use in social, education, health, and employment settings

**Julie Beadle-Brown
and Richard Mills**

TIZARD
University of **Kent**

Pavilion

Understanding and Responding to Autism: The SPELL framework (2nd edition)

A self-study guide for use in social, education, health, and employment settings

Published by:
Pavilion Publishing and Media Ltd
Rayford House
School Road
Hove
East Sussex
BN3 5HX
Tel: 01273 434 943
Fax: 01273 227 308
Email: info@pavpub.com

Published 2018

A catalogue record for this book is available from the British Library.

ISBN: 978-1-912755-19-6

Pavilion is the leading training and development provider and publisher in the health, social care and allied fields, providing a range of innovative training solutions underpinned by sound research and professional values. We aim to put our customers first, through excellent customer service and value.

Authors: Julie Beadle-Brown and Richard Mills
Production editor: Ruth Chalmers, Pavilion Publishing and Media Ltd.
Cover design: Emma Dawe, Pavilion Publishing and Media Ltd.
Page layout and typesetting: Emma Dawe, Pavilion Publishing and Media Ltd.
Printing: Ashford Press

Contents

About the authors

Richard Mills is Research Director at Research Autism, a Research Fellow at CAAR at the University of Bath and Professor of Autism Research at J-CAAR at Taisho University, Tokyo, Japan. He is also a Senior Research Fellow at Bond University, Queensland, Australia and an Associate of AT-Autism London, where he leads on the Synergy programme. From 1991 until 2014 Richard was with the National Autistic Society initially as Director of Services and later as Director of Research. His main practice and research interests include autism and the justice system, programme design and evaluation and working with behaviours of concern. He is an expert member of NICE and was a member of the Guideline Development Groups on Autism in Adults and Behaviours of Concern.

Julie Beadle-Brown is Professor in Intellectual and Developmental Disabilities at the Tizard Centre, University of Kent where she has worked since 1995. She is also Professor in Disability Studies at the Living with Disability Research Centre at La Trobe University in Australia. Her teaching, research and consultancy focuses on improving quality of life children and adults with learning disability and autism and for their families, through high quality services and person-centred approaches such as active support and the SPELL framework. Her work has involved organisations and people across many countries and these experiences have informed the content of this training pack.

Understanding and Responding to Autism: The SPELL framework (2nd edition)

Introduction

Background

Since 1964 The National Autistic Society (NAS) has been supporting families and professionals working with people on the autism spectrum. After years of experience of education and support for autistic children and adults, building on their views and the views of their families – and the evidence from research and practice – a framework emerged that has formed the basis of their training on autism and their provision of services. This framework highlights five key pillars of understanding and good practice through the simple mnemonic 'SPELL':

- **S**tructure
- **P**ositive approaches and expectations
- **E**mpathy
- **L**ow arousal
- **L**inks.

Structure is important for everyone, but autistic people advise that this is vital in reducing anxiety and ambiguity, and can improve self-efficacy and self-esteem leading to better academic and other outcomes and more positive mental health. **Positive approaches** and expectations directly impact on the narrative around autism that for so long was negative and unhelpful and promoted social exclusion. Our emphasis on **Empathy** serves as a reminder that our failure to see the world from the point of view of others creates great problems for the autistic person and is a major barrier to our understanding and responding. **Low arousal** approaches are increasingly recognised as important in reducing the stress associated with complex demands and differences in sensory processing. Finally, **Links** reinforces the need for consistency of approach involving the person, their family and all those involved in the process of providing help or support.

Although many years have passed since this framework was first developed, we believe it has stood the test of time and still offers a valuable way of demystifying, understanding and responding to autism. Of course over time, as with all materials, these have required revision and updating. These 2nd edition materials have tried to incorporate the recommendations from ongoing changes in practice and terminology, evaluation, revising and updating content and resources. We are grateful for the time and effort of all those who contributed to this revision and who have provided quotations.

We particularly acknowledge the ongoing contribution to these materials of many autistic people and to the original work of the late Dr Lorna Wing and her colleague Dr Judith Gould from The NAS; Gary Mesibov and the late Eric Schopler of Division TEACCH and of past and present staff in schools and services for adults.

The overarching aim of this resource is to make the experience, knowledge and skills of working with autistic children and adults available and accessible.

This revision will elaborate on the SPELL framework as a way to both understand and support children and adults on the autism spectrum. It is designed to be used in one of two ways: by individuals studying for their own personal development or by trainers working with a group of staff or carers. The involvement of autistic people in the delivery of training is strongly recommended.

Terminology and underlying ideology

Autism is now regarded as a difference in the way the brain develops (sometimes called a developmental difference) that creates an uneven picture of strengths alongside difficulties, affecting the processing of information, communication, thinking and organisation.

In recent years we have seen a move away from the model of autism as a medical disorder to one where autism is seen as a part of natural human variation, and where autistic people play a much more active role in advocating for recognition and proper support. That is not to dismiss the difficulties faced by autistic children and adults, but to acknowledge that their origins are social in nature and not part of a disease process.

Autism was first described in the scientific literature by Leo Kanner in 1943, although there had been many earlier accounts of the condition. Independently and only really known to the English speaking world much later on, Hans Asperger described a similar yet different group of children in 1944. However, at the time there was no name for the condition, just descriptions of its features. Terms such as 'psychoses' and 'childhood schizophrenia' were used and are still common in other parts of the world. Initially autism was felt to be a mental health disorder akin to schizophrenia and many children and adults were kept in psychiatric institutions. Autism was essentially regarded as a disorder of childhood affecting boys, with little or no thought given to adults or to women and girls.

In the 1960s and early 1970s psychodynamic theories prevailed with parents blamed for 'causing' autism. The dreadful term 'refrigerator mother' was coined by people such as psychoanalyst Bruno Bettelheim. Over time these theories were debunked by research and by the 1980s autism was generally accepted as biological and developmental in nature and incorporated into official diagnostic manuals as a specific disorder. It was also seen as a life-long condition and not something a child would 'grow out of'. Nowadays, mainly thanks to autistic advocates and the concept of neurodiversity, autism is seen more as 'a way of being' – 'different not less' – and that with opportunity, understanding and reasonable adjustments the future for autistic individuals is much more promising.

It is also increasingly accepted, thanks to the work of the late British psychiatrist Lorna Wing and her colleagues, that although autistic people may share many of the same characteristics, autism is best described as a spectrum – that its boundaries are not clear cut and can appear in as many different ways as there are children or adults with the condition; there are no two people are exactly alike.

This resource will use the terms 'children and adults on the autism spectrum', or 'autistic children and adults', but these are synonymous with autism spectrum disorders, autism spectrum conditions, autism and Asperger syndrome.

Recent research by psychiatrist Christopher Gillberg in Sweden even suggests that autism as a discreet condition is relatively rare and that children and adults will show clusters of other neurodevelopmental difficulties such as attention deficit hyperactivity disorder (ADHD), dyspraxia, dyslexia, Tourette syndrome and seizure disorders, including epilepsy, which further blurs the boundaries.

Overall, it is the narrative around autism that has shown most significant change, moving from 'devastating disability' to neurological difference – with strengths as well as difficulties – in need of support and understanding rather than 'treatment'.

The approach taken in this resource reflects a person-centred approach; it draws from the experience of autistic people and their families. In order to support the person, it is necessary to understand the individual and how they see the world and how the world impacts on them. This is the essence of the approach.

Part 1: Understanding autism provides the information to develop this knowledge and understanding. Only then can one apply the SPELL framework described in detail in **Part 2: Supporting children and adults on the autism spectrum**. The SPELL framework is not the only element of good support for people with autism; using other strategies is essential to helping people with autism reach their potential. These approaches will be outlined in **Annex 6**

with information provided for further reading. Training on these approaches is available elsewhere so the aim of this resource is to help people make the links between the SPELL framework and these other approaches, and to think about the wider context of people's lives as well as the day-to-day needs of the individual.

The SPELL framework fits neatly into the group of person-centred approaches described in Mansell *et al* (2005) which are relevant to people with intellectual and developmental disabilities. Person-centred action helps staff to work positively with individuals and learn about their individual strengths and preferences and, as such, possible directions and aspirations to feed into planning processes. Planning informs longer-term directions for people and helps to ensure that action develops and does not become stale.

In order to help people think about their future, to plan and have dreams and aspirations, it is essential that there is an inclusive and positive narrative and that those working with autistic people really get to know them and know how their autism and the world around them impacts on their lives, as well as the strategies that work best to enable and empower them. A positive and inclusive approach is focused on enabling people to participate in all aspects of their lives and the experience of being respected, valued and listened to. So often what we hear described as 'challenging behaviour' is a result of our failure to understand the person and their experience of the world.

This positive, enabling but empathetic approach is at the heart of this resource.

Who can use this resource?

This handbook which provides a self-study route through the content for anyone who works with or supports a child or adult on the autism spectrum. The book guides the reader through the materials and when to watch particular videos and do the various exercises and activities, to encourage independent thinking and learning. The annexes, video clips and audio are all available to download online from https://www.pavpub.com/understanding-and-responding-to-autism-self-study-resources/.

A copy of the book is also included in the *Understanding and Responding to Autism: The SPELL framework* training resource. The training pack is designed so that those who have experience and knowledge in the field of autism can train larger groups of people within their own organisations or to other organisations. The self-study guide mirrors the trainer's script from the pack

Understanding and Responding to Autism: The SPELL framework (2nd edition)
© Pavilion Publishing and Media Ltd and its licensors 2018.

and provides the background information needed to run the training, provided in a convenient format.

We recommend that learners using the handbook for self-study follow the materials in the order in which they are written, but you can do so all at once or over several sessions. It should take between five and seven hours to complete, depending on reading speed and how many videos you watch. Recommended further reading for people who would like to continue to learn more is provided at the end, on p109.

Learners should take any opportunity to discuss the ideas and their learning with a supervisor, more experienced support person, or even with fellow learners following the training materials. This is particularly important where staff teams are being trained – even if they follow the self-study route primarily, opportunities should be provided by their organisation for discussion and group work around the concepts with a focus on the people they support. This is important for consistent attitudes and practice across the team.

Part 1: Understanding autism

This module will cover the following topics:

- Terminology
- Context
- Cause, prevalence and diagnosis
- Core characteristics of autism
- The sensory world of autism
- Other features and the strengths of autism
- Underlying mechanisms
- Personal experiences
- Introduction to the SPELL framework

Before reading through the content below, start by taking the quiz in **Annex 1**. Don't worry if you find that you are ticking lots of 'don't know' or 'maybe' answers for now. By the time you have finished working through this module you should be able to answer all of these questions.

Terminology

In the past, terms such as 'childhood psychoses', 'childhood schizophrenia' and so on were used. In some countries, autism in adulthood is only now starting to be recognised with a tendency for adults to be diagnosed with mental health conditions such as schizophrenia or personality disorder rather than with autism.

In the UK, America and Australia, the most common terms are 'people with autism', 'people on the autism spectrum', 'people with an autism spectrum disorder' or 'people with an autism spectrum condition', recognising the diversity of the condition.

A study conducted by researchers at University College London and the National Autistic Society in 2015 (Kenny *et al*, 2016) found that across the autism community there was no single preferred way of referring to autism although the terms 'autism' and 'on the autism spectrum', and to a lesser extent 'autism spectrum disorder', received the most acceptance overall. Some people stated a preference for the term 'disorder' as they felt that they have a disability based on impairments and without a diagnosis based on this they are unable to get help. The term 'autistic' was preferred over the term 'person with autism' by autistic adults, parents, other family members and friends

As such the terms used in these materials will be 'children and adults on the autism spectrum' and 'autistic'.

Context

Some of us are better at knowing how other people 'tick' and have few problems in relating to others, but struggle with technical stuff. We grasp the big picture but may be bored by detail. We may be described as extrovert. We seem to know instinctively what other people are thinking and may be popular and comfortable with a wide circle of friends and have a range of interests.

Some of us are better at knowing how things work and may have special interests or technical skills but may find it difficult to relate to others. We are better at dealing with detail than with the 'big picture'. We may be described as more introvert. We may find it hard to understand instinctively what other people may be thinking or what they are planning to do. Our friendships are more geared toward interests we share with others and we tend to be more comfortable with one or two people than in a larger group. Some of us are a bit of both or in between.

These behaviours usually indicate an underlying neurodiversity, i.e. our brains can develop and then work in different ways. As such, we are all part of a spectrum. For some people, the swing to one side or the other is so extreme that they are diagnosed with a condition such as autism or ADHD. For the rest of us the neurodiversity is less extreme.

It is important to keep the idea of a spectrum of diversity in your head while you continue to follow this resource. We are all different in how we think, feel and operate in different circumstances. We all have strengths and weaknesses.

It is important to note here that autism isn't a new condition as such. It has been described for centuries; individuals who would now be likely to receive a diagnosis of an autism spectrum disorder have existing for many years in both historical accounts and in mythology. Itard's description of 'Victor the Wild Boy of Averyon' being the best known. You will also hear people talking about some of the greatest minds and artists in history as perhaps being on the autism spectrum – Einstein, Darwin, Mozart, da Vinci. More recently scientific advancements in computers are also said to have been developed by individuals with autistic characteristics with high-level abilities in science and technology.

Autism was first described scientifically in 1943 by psychiatrist Leo Kanner. However, in 1944, but unknown to most of the English-speaking world until the work was introduced by Lorna Wing in the 1980s, Austrian paediatrician Hans Asperger (pronounced with a hard 'g') described a similar, yet distinctly different, group of children but with good language and of average or above intelligence.

The word 'autistic' was used by both Kanner and Asperger and comes from the Greek word 'autos' meaning 'self'. Concepts of autism have developed through research pioneers from armchair theory to science-based understanding. Our understanding has also benefitted from the input of autistic people themselves. Now it is described as a spectrum, with 'core features' thought to be common to all individuals but to differing degrees.

Autism is generally accepted as being present from birth (although it may not be obvious initially) and affects several aspects of development. It continues into adulthood although can manifest itself in different ways at different ages and in different people. As noted, there is neurodiversity in the autism population as well as the general population. No two children or adults are the same. We will come back to look at the different manifestations later.

Most if not all of us will engage in some behaviours that if we did them more often or couldn't stop them when asked or when we needed to, would be likely to have other people wondering if we were on the autism spectrum.

If we walk down the main street in our local town and look at people as they walk past us or towards us, we may see behaviour that looks distinctly like that of autistic people – people apparently in a world of their own, not paying attention to others, not making eye contact, bumping into people and then getting annoyed, moody or shouting because they have had enough of shopping, having temper tantrums because they didn't get what they want – but they may be on the phone, listening to their MP3 player or are simply afraid to make eye contact in case it sends the wrong message.

Key learning points

■ **Autism is not new and our understanding is continually increasing due to better science and the input of autistic people themselves.**

■ **Autism is highly diverse and personalised approaches are essential.**

■ **Most of us show autistic traits without being diagnosed as autistic.**

Exercise 1

Have a think about what you are doing with your hands and your feet while you are reading this resource. You might find you are twiddling a pencil, or your hair. Perhaps you are biting your nails or a pencil. Perhaps you are tapping your foot or jiggling your leg up and down. How long can you sit and read without having to get up for a pace about, or a cup of tea?

Cause, prevalence and diagnosis

Causes of autism

There are many theories of autism and few are conclusive. It is known to relate to brain development and not upbringing, although life opportunities will affect outcome – especially in education, relationships and dealing with stress and anxiety. Autism is not caused by poor parenting.

Studies on the neurology of autism are also not conclusive or consistent and research has been slow in identifying specific genes and brain regions implicated in autism. This may be because these genes and brain regions are also implicated in a range of other conditions and attributes such as giftedness.

There are some theories related to genetic predisposition triggered by an environmental event such as MMR or toxins and, although there remains much debate on the issue, there is no research evidence to support this. Such research also raises important ethical issues, such as whether autism can be prevented, and autistic people and those who appreciate the important role autistic people play in many aspects of our society, are very concerned about the implications.

Understanding and Responding to Autism: The SPELL framework (2nd edition)

Key learning points

■ **Autism is not a single condition. There is no single cause for autism and the slow progress of research in this area and the diversity of the condition suggests that this is unlikely.**

■ **Autism is not caused by poor parenting although experience of human relationships is critical to outcome.**

■ **It is also an area where ethics play a significant part and one that is sensitive to autistic people. The absence of known causation leaves people vulnerable to dubious treatments and damaging theories.**

How many people are on the spectrum

Recent research in the UK has shown that approximately one in 100 children have an autism spectrum condition. A study by Baird *et al* (2006) found that 116 children in every 1,000 had an autism spectrum diagnosis. In 2009 the Department of Health commissioned a survey of adults and confirmed that one in 100 adults had an autism spectrum condition and that this was true across the lifespan (Brugha *et al*, 2009). Prevalence rates vary across countries due to a number of factors, not least the status of diagnostic and treatment services.

In terms of gender distribution, the prevalence of autism in boys/men is greater than in girls/women. The precise ratio differs by subgroup and there still remains some debate as to the gender distribution. For example, early work by Lotter and Wing and Gould found that there are there were approximately four boys for every girl with what was known as 'classic autism', but Gillberg found that there were approximately 15 boys for every girl with Asperger syndrome.

There is emerging evidence that the latter might be an underestimation of the number of women with Asperger syndrome and that women might be less likely to be diagnosed as they appear to cope better socially so their difficulties are less obvious. However, there is as yet no research evidence to confirm this and it may be due to the type of diagnostic tool used.

Key learning points

- **The overall prevalence of all forms of autism in the UK is around 1 in 100.**

- **In the USA it is said to be higher at around 1 in 88 but most other countries are around the UK level or with fewer diagnosed.**

- **Prevalence relates to awareness and the status of diagnostic, clinical and therapeutic services.**

How is autism diagnosed

Criteria and measures for diagnosing autism have changed over time. Since the early 1970s these have broadened to include more people who do not also have an intellectual disability and those who have higher levels of verbal communication. As noted earlier, diagnosis is currently based on observed behaviours and characteristics, not on any blood or genetic test or brain scan.

Autism is usually characterised by core features that involve the presence of unusual developmental and behavioural features alongside the absence of usual developmental and behavioural features. It is usually accompanied by other co-occurring problems such as anxiety, epilepsy, learning difficulties and so on.

This is not a formal clinical diagnosis but summarises the nature of the condition and how it is presented. Which developmental and behaviour features are absent or unusual will vary from individual to individual and may also change across time for some people. For further information on how autism is diagnosed clinically see **Annex 10**.

Characteristics of autism

What does autism look like?

Thinking activity

Watch the A is for Autism film. Turn the speakers up as loud as you can without getting in trouble with the neighbours. As you watch the film, note down what you think are important points and how the film impacts you.

Understanding and Responding to Autism: The SPELL framework (2nd edition)
© Pavilion Publishing and Media Ltd and its licensors 2018.

https://www.youtube.com/watch?v=zxt3FBVq8Jg

Notes and reflections from A is for Autism video

Once you have done this, go to **Annex 3** to see some of our reflections about the video.

Impact of autism on the individual

We will move on now to look in more detail about how autistic people are affected by the condition. In particular we will look at:

- communication difficulties
- intense interests
- high order skills in specific areas
- repetitiveness
- hypo- and/or hyper-sensitivity/sensory processing difficulties
- high levels of personal stress and anxiety.

As we go through these sections it is important to keep in mind how the characteristics of autism impact on individuals, and in particular on their vulnerability and quality of life. In particular, autistic people are often denied opportunities and rights due to being perceived as 'different', and this can also result in them being bullied. Secondly, autistic people are at risk of being misunderstood and as a result treated as mentally disordered. Finally, due to social and communication difficulties and difficulties understanding how people think or feel, they often have difficulty making and keeping friends and thus experience fewer relationships. This can increase the risk of social isolation, of bullying and the possibility of mental health issues.

> **❛ I'd find rocket science infinitely easier to understand than love. ❜**
>
> **Joe Powell**

Key learning points

- **It is important to recognise the vulnerability of people who are seen as different.**
- **There is potential for social exclusion and isolation, especially later in life.**

Social and communication difficulties

First of all, it is important to recognise that communication is not the same as speech. For many reasons, some autistic people may not speak, but this does not mean they are unable to communicate. If we learn how to listen, everyone can communicate.

Where speech exists it may be unusual – this is often in the 'social' use of speech, for example maintaining a two-way conversation about something that is not a special interest of the individual on the autism spectrum. There can be difficulties using and understanding pronouns, for example 'I', 'you', 'me', and there can be idiosyncratic speech, where the person makes up words that mean something to them but not to other people, for example a child asking to 'go on green riding' to mean 'can we go to the swings in the park'. Speech can also be repetitive or echolalic, i.e. where the child or adult repeats what has just been said to them or what has been said to them in the past. There can also be difficulties with 'wh' words – 'what', 'why' and 'where' ('What is this?' 'Where are you going?' 'What did you do?' 'Why did you do that?').

There can be differences in pitch and tone: some people talk in a very soft voice that is very difficult to hear; some in a very loud voice that resounds around their environment; some people talk with a high pitched or sing-song voice; others use

Understanding and Responding to Autism: The SPELL framework (2nd edition)
© Pavilion Publishing and Media Ltd and its licensors 2018.

special voices in particular circumstances; some people might have 'warbling' or 'tremoring' voices; very commonly people have no intonation and speak in a monotone voice. In some people, formal, pedantic speech can be very noticeable but can also be misunderstood as being cheeky or awkward.

There can be a marked difference between expressive language (what is said) and receptive language (what is understood). This can often result in substantial misunderstandings of the individual's level of ability.

Processing of language may be also slower – spoken language is abstract and temporary and you need knowledge of vocabulary and what words mean. This can often be difficult for autistic people.

Key learning points

- **Not being able to speak is not the same as having nothing to say.**
- **All behaviour can be communication.**
- **Receptive speech and slow processing are often major issues in autism.**

Many autistic people have difficulty initiating interactions and keeping conversations going. They show a particular difficulty making small talk. If it is not something they are interested in then it is hard for them to talk about it. Many more able autistic people express this as a key issue for them.

> *'I am completely unable to navigate small talk. I am great at introductions, public speaking, etc. I just can't seem to have a conversation that works. Worse, I am often totally misunderstood.'*
>
> Walter, self employed watchmaker
> (an excerpt from Aspergers on the Job, by Rudy Simone, 2010).

Autistic people also have difficulties with non-verbal communication, for example, they have difficulty using and understanding facial expressions and using tone of voice to convey meaning or emotion. Body language is usually a mystery to them. Even those who appear to be very able in many ways often struggle with reading body language and facial expression and knowing how to respond. This can cause considerable anxiety as it makes predicting behaviour in others even more difficult.

Autistic people often have difficulty with understanding social context and regulating their behaviour and responses accordingly. They can behave in a way that is seen by others as strange or inappropriate. They might quite openly and often very loudly, comment on someone's physical appearance. For example, 'Mum, look at that very fat man over there' shouted in the middle of the supermarket – people are more tolerant if a three year old says something like this but if a 15 year old says it then it will be viewed as rude and offensive.

People on the autism spectrum may have difficulties understanding jokes and sarcasm. Unless these are very obvious they may be misinterpreted as criticism or rudeness.

They sometimes have difficulties with pronouns (for example confusing or reversing he/she; you/me) and also find that abstract concepts are particular difficult to process and understand. They also have difficulty with common phrases and sayings unless these can be 'literally' understood.

Literal understanding

Difficulties understanding commonly used phrases that are abstract and do not have a clear literal meaning are widespread in autistic individuals. The English language in particular is littered with metaphors and expressions which just aren't 'true':

- It is raining cats and dogs.
- I have eyes in the back of my head.
- Have you got ants in your pants?
- Are your eyes bigger than your belly?

I am sure you can think of more examples of such phrases that would be difficult for someone with a literal understanding. Try to think about what the person might do if they didn't understand phrases such as 'Mary was crying her eyes out'; in this case it wouldn't be surprising to find the autistic person distressed, on the floor at Mary's feet, looking for her eyes!

However, literal understanding doesn't just apply to metaphors or sayings. In fact, many autistic people often learn familiar metaphors and the true meaning behind them and realise they should not be taken literally (although sometimes they need continual reassurance that they have correctly understood, for example:

'I knew a person who whenever anyone at the day centre mentioned babysitting he would interrupt them and say, "But that doesn't mean you sit on a real baby", and staff then had to reassure him that he was right – babysitting does not mean you sit on a real baby.'

There are many phrases that we use every day that can be difficult for people who only have a concrete, literal understanding. For example, when we say 'I'll do it in a minute', an autistic person might stand and count '1,2,3,4… 59,60. Now?' Another example might be 'Pull the door behind you when you leave, John' – you might find John standing looking at the hinges wondering how on earth he is going to detach it to pull it behind him going down the street.

Exercise 2

Make a list of at least 10 phrases that you use every day that you think might be misleading or confusing for people who only understand the literal meaning of figurative expressions. For each phrase, try to predict what the person's response might be. You might be able to do this by drawing on your own experience with someone you know. In particular, try to think of examples of a time you were not sure why someone acted a certain way until you realised that you or someone else had said something that the person had misunderstood due to their literal understanding.

Remember, literal understanding extends to the written word and to images as well as the spoken word. We only have to think about some of the road signs we have in the UK, which due to an absence of punctuation or a word having several meanings can cause confusion e.g. 'SLOW MEN AT WORK' or 'HEAVY PLANT CROSSING'.

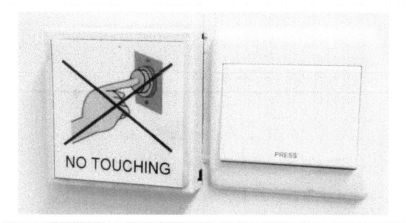

Figure 1 illustrates the sign that a school in Singapore had to put over their fire alarm buttons after they had weeks of the fire alarms constantly going off. The box (now hidden) clearly states, in big green writing, 'Press Here' so the children did... over and over again!

In general, we find that when autistic people do something that might seem strange to us, it is usually helpful to think about what we just said or what cues the environment is providing. On many occasions, we find that we have inadvertently told the person to do what they have done.

All children and adults on the autism spectrum have some form of difficulty in interacting with other people – it is one of the most defining characteristics of autism. However, as for communication, there is a wide variety of ways that these difficulties present, which vary from individual to individual and which can change with age and experience. For example:

I went to visit someone at a day centre in Berkshire many years ago. I rang the bell and a young man came bounding to the door and opened it. Before I could speak, he said to me, without making eye contact, 'Do you drink Guinness?' It turned out that this young man was autistic and had a special interest (some might have labelled it an obsession) about Guinness and asked everyone who came to the day centre whether they liked Guinness.

■ People may appear sociable but attempts at social behaviour can be seen as 'strange', naïve or inappropriate. People can be unaware of the impact of the behaviour on others.

Understanding and Responding to Autism: The SPELL framework (2nd edition)
© Pavilion Publishing and Media Ltd and its licensors 2018.

- On the other hand, some people may be passive in their social interactions – responding to physical or even social contact but not initiating contact with others. Young children who are passive are often quite liked by other children as they are often more willing to play the passive roles in games – and to follow the rules set down by other children.

- Some people may avoid social contact – usually because they find it unpredictable and stressful.

- Where they have tried to participate in social interactions they may lose confidence when social approaches are rebuffed in some way and they then may withdraw or avoid future interactions. This might be as simple as trying to initiate an interaction that is ignored.

- Many people find one-to-one social situations easier – groups can be very stressful but interestingly, presenting at conferences to large audiences may not be – **why do you think this might be?**

As noted earlier, people may have problems with unwritten social rules and social conventions e.g. how close you should stand to another person. This is particularly difficult as these rules may vary in different contexts. This makes it very difficult to operate in a social world without being seen as different and odd or they might come across as rude when they are just being factual.

Rules are important as they give clarity and control to the person and the absence of rules may be highly stressful. However it is not always possible to have rules for life – and this in itself can be very stressful.

Thinking activity

Think about an autistic person you know and make a list of the difficulties that they have in terms of their social interactions and communication. Can you think of examples where someone you know fails to understand 'normal' social conventions? What are the consequences of this?

Thinking activity answers

Key learning point

■ **Do not underestimate how literal people can be or how stressful new interactions can be in particular.**

Exercise 3

Find someone to help you with this. Stand at opposite ends of a room and walk towards each other, each person stopping when you find you are beginning to feel that you are uncomfortably close. Did you both stop at the same time? Who became uncomfortable first? Would it be different if you were with someone you didn't know? What type of situations do you find that you are uncomfortable in with other people? Why do you think you feel uncomfortable?

Many autistic people are sublimely unaware of social conventions, such as personal space. They will often come right up to someone and perhaps even touch their face. They might flaunt psychological barriers such as going behind a counter in a shop or into a bathroom when someone else is using it or perhaps undressing in front of strangers. At the same time, and we are going to come back to this later, they might be over-sensitive to people coming into their personal space.

There are times when standing very close to people is appropriate (or at least unavoidable). Can you think of some examples? One example would be on a tube or train at rush hour. Although we can have rules and social conventions, sometimes we have to break these rules. This can be very difficult for autistic people who find it difficult to apply different rules in different situations. These responses are also determined to a degree by culture; in some cultures personal space may be less of an issue, in others personal space should not be compromised under any circumstances.

Understanding and Responding to Autism: The SPELL framework (2nd edition)

This final section under social and communication difficulties looks at the issue of empathy, joint attention and play. In this section we distinguish between what we call 'instinctive empathy' and what we call 'intellectual empathy'. Instinctive empathy may be impaired in autistic people but intellectual empathy can be heightened. So for example, people may find it difficult to know how or why someone is upset at that particular point in time but they understand that people can be upset in particular circumstances, and that things they say and do can cause other people to be upset or offended. This can cause additional stress and anxiety as people worry about whether they might be saying or have said things that might have offended someone.

Secondly empathy is a two-way street – we need to have empathy for the autistic view and we need to understand how people think, feel and experience the world and what is helpful and what is not. If we don't, we can cause people substantial difficulties.

Joint or shared attention or play may be difficult for many autistic people and, in particular, pretend play can be impaired. Often autistic children are observed to play more repetitively with toys, sometimes engaging in very elaborate routines. Children can sometimes learn to look like they are pretending when playing on their own but often this will be a learnt routine that they have established with their dolls or cars. Many autistic children find it very hard to play pretend games with other children where they have to take account of the other person's ideas and pretence. Often autistic children are observed to play in parallel with other children but not jointly. However, autistic children *do* play and can engage in a wide range of imaginative activities if given the support and encouragement to do so.

Finally, issues with eye gaze and eye contact are often associated with autism. Many people do have problems with eye gaze – sometimes people may be perceived by others as too intense (staring); others may instinctively avoid gaze; for many, eye contact is experienced as aversive, and for some even painful.

It is important to remember that despite commonly used strategies for trying to get children's attention, eye contact is not related to paying attention. You don't need to be making eye contact in order to hear what people are saying. For many autistic children and adults, being made to look in your eyes or even at your face (with all its confusing information), will make it impossible for them to actually listen and pay attention to what you are saying.

Issues with eye contact are not just related to autism – children and adults with other conditions also find eye contact difficult. In addition, there are cultural differences related to the appropriateness of making direct eye contact. Many autistic people (in particular, girls) are very good at looking like they are making eye contact, but they are often actually looking at a point on your nose or just above your eyes. The fact that people appear to make eye contact therefore can be misleading – we hear many stories about people being told they can't be on the autism spectrum because they make eye contact. We have to look at the whole picture for people otherwise we miss important information.

Video

Watch this video from young people with a range of conditions telling their teachers how they can help them by understanding them better.
https://www.youtube.com/watch?v=lTMLzXzgB_s

Key learning points

■ **Empathy is a two-way street – non-autistic people cause many problems for autistic people by not seeing their point of view.**

■ **Autistic children derive great pleasure through self-directed play but it might look unusual to the observer.**

■ **It was thought that eye contact was essential to developing socially and academically. This is now known to be untrue.**

■ **Eye contact can be highly aversive and people should not be forced to do it.**

Special interests and repetitive behaviour

1. Special interests

Autistic people can have special interests that are often intense (e.g. dinosaurs, railway timetables, buses, UFOs, recycling, street names, historical figures, shoes, film stars or musicians, make-up etc). Special interests might also be things like amassing and internalising information on a particular topic, taking apart and fixing electronic equipment, knowing the flags of every country.

Special interests may be absorbing – sometimes to the exclusion of everything else.

Sometimes special interests can be sensitive and cause offence in certain situations – e.g. collections such as Nazi memorabilia. However, for the most part special interests are extremely useful for getting to know people, building rapport, motivating people and building skills.

Understanding and Responding to Autism: The SPELL framework (2nd edition)
© Pavilion Publishing and Media Ltd and its licensors 2018.

Figure 2: This photo shows how a teacher used ducks, the child's special interest, to help her in learning numeracy.

PIKACHU

Pikachu is like a _____. Its body is _____

and it has got some _____.

Its ears are also a bit_____. Its attack is _____.

Solution: Pikachu is like a mouse. Its body is yellow and it has got some brown stripes. Its ears are also a bit black. Its cheeks are red. Its tail is like lightning. Its attack is lightning.

CHARMANDER

Charmander is like a _____. Its body is _____

_____, It's _____ kind, so its tail has got a _____

_____. Its attack is _____.

Figure 3: An example of how a child's interest in Pokémon was used to help with literacy.

Thinking activity

Think about the people that you know and see if you can make a list of the sorts of special interests that they have. Have these stayed the same over time? What is the impact of their special interest? Can you use the special interests as a tool for motivation?

2. Preference for sameness and predictability

Many children and adults on the autism spectrum find it difficult to cope with change, especially changes that are unexpected. For some people, the small changes are sometimes worse than the big changes – for example, a child might be able to cope with having a different teacher in the classroom but not the fact that she moved the stapler from one side of the desk to the other. Transitions of any type can be difficult for many autistic people. These can seem very minor changes to us but the impact on autistic people can be substantial.

3. Difficulties shifting attention to a new task

In addition to difficulties with change in general, many autistic people (as well as people with ADHD, dyspraxia and indeed people with damage to the front part of their brain) can find it very difficult to move from one task to another, particularly if they feel they haven't finished the first task. Multi-tasking is particularly difficult for autistic people.

4. Perfectionism

Many of those on the autism spectrum not only find it difficult to change to a different task but also find it difficult if they cannot finish a task or a routine to their satisfaction. This may often be to a higher level than is actually expected from them by others (e.g. teachers, parents, employers). This can be very subtle in some people but in others it can take a more obvious form – for example, a child who will not accept a broken biscuit.

5. Repetitive behaviours and speech

Some children and adults also show repetitive behaviours and speech – e.g. asking the same questions over and over again (remember Temple Grandin in the A is for Autism video – 'why are the streets lights coming on…') repetitive actions and routines e.g. having to spin three times before sitting down at the table or playing

Understanding and Responding to Autism: The SPELL framework (2nd edition)
© Pavilion Publishing and Media Ltd and its licensors 2018.

with a toy over and over again, adjusting their belt again and again. Sometimes, these repetitive behaviours can appear obsessive and compulsive and autistic people are sometimes misdiagnosed as just having obsessive compulsive behaviours.

Example

I was once observing in a service where there were several autistic people living. They were not very engaged and I got quite excited when I thought a lady was tidying out her handbag. However, as I watched her do it for the third time, taking things out in the same order each time, I realised that it was a repetitive behaviour.

Example

I was told about a man who had been referred for an assessment for autism and was visited by an advocate who was going to help him to understand the process and to be able to get to the assessment. The man had not been able to leave the house for years as he had to check every door, window, make sure the cooker was switched off etc. When he had finished he had to check it all again. He was unable to move on from the checking routine as he was anxious about not having done something. The solution was simple – his advocate helped him to make a list so that he could tick it off as he did it and then he had a visual cue that he had actually checked everything. At this point he was able to leave the house. This is an example of visual structure which we will come to in Part 2.

Example

Sometimes, however, having a special interest might not be as useful as we might think. Another man had a special interest in aircraft – the 'ideal' job came up for him in air traffic control as a trainee but he could not cope with the temptation to only follow his favourite airlines and so lost his job.

Key learning point

- **Special interests are important but sometimes have to be managed as they can become disabling – such as hoarding behaviour.**

The sensory world of autism

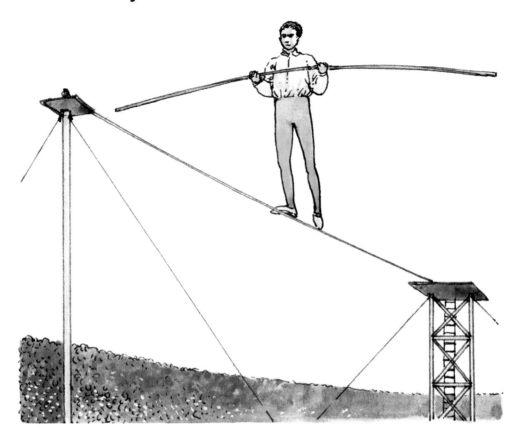

1. Sensory sensitivities

Although only recently featuring in the diagnostic criteria for autism, research has shown than almost everyone who is on the autism spectrum has sensory sensitivities. This could be multiple sensitivities and can affect all the senses. People can be sensitive to things that involve:

■ visual processes, such as sensitivity to light or to particular colours

■ hearing, for example, loud noises, noises of a particular frequency or discordant noises (such as the rest of the class practising the recorder!)

■ smell, for example strong perfumes, air fresheners, fresh flowers

■ taste, such as things that have a particular type of flavour or texture

■ touch, for example the feeling of clothes or particular materials.

These sensory differences extend to balance and the sense of gravity, and to the proprioceptive system.

People can be 'hyper' (over) sensitive to sensory stimuli. This can result in the person withdrawing and seeking to avoid sensory simulation. People can experience aversive, sometimes even painful reactions to sensory stimulation e.g. painful hearing, difficulty with touch, reaction to smells, e.g. food cooking. Too much stimulation can result in sensory overload and the person can be overwhelmed.

Sometimes people can be 'hypo' (under) sensitive to sensory stimuli. They are likely to seek sensory stimulation and are likely to engage in behaviours that provide repetitive stimulation, such as spinning, bouncing, manipulating objects, making certain sounds, etc. Sometimes this can go as far as self-injurious behaviours, such as head banging, self-biting, picking scabs, regurgitating.

Autistic people can have 'low registration' – the best example of this is low registration for pain. Some children and autistic adults can be hurt severely and not report any pain at all. You may have heard stories of people who had walked around for several days on a broken ankle until someone eventually noticed it was swollen and bruised. Firm touch is often much more pleasant to people on the spectrum whereas this can contrast to having very low threshold for gentle touch or a much more minor injury, which can produce a very extreme reaction.

Of course, people can be both hyper and hypo sensitive, for example liking or even needing very strong stimulation (swinging, spinning, rocking, etc) and deep pressure on the outside of their body whilst at the same time only being able to eat bland, smooth, cool food.

2. Sensory processing difficulties

Autistic people (and those with other conditions) often have delayed processing of sensory information. You may have heard people say that you should give an autistic person an instruction and then wait 20 seconds before asking again. Our natural reaction when people don't respond immediately is to repeat the request or question and often we change what we say to make it 'easier'. However, for someone who needs longer to process information they might only just have begun to process the first instruction and then you ask again in a slightly different way, meaning they have to start all over again and effectively process a different set of words. Twenty seconds seems a very long time but often if you give people long enough they will respond and will get less frustrated in the process. For some children and adults, the processing delay may be even more extensive. Problems with processing sensory information also extend to perceptual problems, for example, processing things from a particular perspective (like trying to imitate someone's actions when they are opposite the person might be harder than imitating actions where they are facing the same direction). Understanding scales (for example distance or weight) can also be difficult.

3. Screening out unwanted stimuli

Autistic people, as well as those with other conditions such as ADHD, have difficulty screening out unwanted sensory information, so if more than one thing is going on around them they might often choose the 'wrong' thing to pay attention to. It is thought that sensory processing problems are at the heart of many other difficulties, such as sleep, eating, attention problems and self-injury.

Autistic people will often appear to be paying attention to something other than what they are meant to be attending to. They will be hearing the bus go past on the road rather than what the teacher has just said. Things that may seem insignificant to us may be much louder or much more difficult for people who are on the autism spectrum.

Figure 4: This young man can cope with the visual stimuli in the aquarium environment if he cuts out the auditory stimulation.

Understanding and Responding to Autism: The SPELL framework (2nd edition)
© Pavilion Publishing and Media Ltd and its licensors 2018.

For some people, sensory sensitivities and sensory processing difficulties can become so extreme that they go into sensory overload and can no longer cope with it. At this point they may engage in what might be considered 'challenging behaviour' or they may just go and hide under a duvet or in the cushions on the sofa. So-called 'tantrums' in public places are commonly due to sensory overload.

'Behaviours' that may linked to sensory processing

- Sniffing.
- Running away.
- Refusal to wear clothes.
- Covering ears.
- Screaming.
- Humming.
- Eating inedible things (PICA).
- Spinning.
- Rocking.
- Pacing.
- Smearing.
- Regurgitation.
- Tiptoe walking.
- Self-slapping or biting.

It is important to understand the reason for these behaviours – why is the child or adult doing them? Sometimes we might need a more in-depth analysis to help us know whether a behaviour is related to sensory needs or not. Without this information about the 'function' a behaviour plays for a person, then it can be hard to develop an intervention that will work.

Some further examples of the nature and impact of sensory sensitivities and differences can be found in many of the accounts written by autistic individuals. Steven Shore (2003) also writes about sensory sensitivities in his book *Beyond the Walls*.

Watch the video 'Mason on an autistic stimming bender'. Try to notice all the different ways he stimulates himself and how difficult it is for his mum to try to interrupt his stimming: http://www.youtube.com/watch?v=X78Zt-ehfKU

Tito Mukopadhayay

Tito (who is non-verbal and severely autistic) describes in his book *Beyond the Silence* (2000) why he spins. Notice how clear his reasons are:

> 'When you are trying to think blue
> And end up thinking black
> You can be sure to be frustrated
> Time and again it happens to me
> And I get quite helpless
> Otherwise why should I get up and spin myself
> Spinning my body
> Brings some sort of harmony to my thoughts
> So that I can centrifuge away all of the black thoughts
> I realise that the faster I spin
> The faster I drive away the black
> When I am sure that even the last speck of black
> Has gone away from me…
>
> …..Then I spin back in the opposite direction
> And pull the blue thoughts into myself
> It depends on how much blue I want
> If I want more blue I have to spin faster
> Otherwise not so fast
> It's just like being a fan
> The trouble is when I stop spinning
> My body scatters
> And it's so difficult to collect it together again.'

Tito also explains why he chooses not to speak – notice how the primary reason is to do with sensory issues more than social or communicative issues.

> 'When I participate in a dialogue my senses shatter so it becomes very difficult to continue writing. Writing the next word is like rowing a canoe upstream when all the pressures and forces are working against you, against my hand holding the pencil. What would I do then? I would get up in the middle of a sentence, which I began, walk away, recharge my senses with some environmental distraction, and then come back. I would pick up my pencil again and continue with my sentence, thus completing it.'

Video

Watch and reflect on the video 'In my language':
https://www.youtube.com/watch?v=JnylM1hI2jc

Key learning points

- **It is important to listen to autistic children and adults, using whatever way they prefer to communicate.**

- **We need to inform the help we give people through empathy for the way the person sees the world.**

- **Understanding the autistic experience, including the person's sensory sensitivities and processing difficulties, shapes attitudes toward them and their behaviour.**

Exercise 4

The audio recording labelled Soundtrack for Exercise 4 (go to https://www.pavpub.com/understanding-and-responding-to-autism-self-study-resources/ to listen) will give you instructions to draw a diagram. Try to follow the instructions and draw the diagram either in the space below or on a separate piece of paper. You can also switch on your TV or radio at the same time. Start listening to the recording and drawing when you are ready.

When you have finished you can check **Annex 4** to see what the diagram was supposed to look like!

Reflection on Exercise 4

How did you feel about doing this? Did you find it harder to concentrate?

Think about how you feel when trying to listen to someone else speaking to you in a very noisy environment – e.g. at a party, concert, nightclub? Have you ever found yourself feeling frustrated or embarrassed because you had no idea what the person was saying to you and worried that might be nodding and shaking your head in the wrong places?

Think about when you were first learning to drive – how did you respond when people tried to talk to you or were making noise in the back seat while you were driving? Even once we are experienced drivers, if we are in a new place and trying to navigate and drive, having children being noisy in the back seat can make us annoyed or lose concentration.

Other features and the strengths of autism

Co-occurring conditions

Some co-occurring conditions are related to autism, others are completely separate and anyone can have them. Recently there has been some focus on what is sometimes called the syndrome mix of neuropsychological conditions. Although there is little information on how often some of these conditions occur along with autistic spectrum disorders, it is generally accepted that children for whom autism is the primary diagnosis can also have other neuropsychological difficulties and conditions, in particular ADHD, dyspraxia, mood disorders, dyslexia and sensory processing and integration problems. People may not have a diagnosis of these conditions but can be affected by them and can often benefit from treatment aimed at the co-occurring condition.

Autism is also commonly accompanied by an intellectual (learning) disability, although some recent research has suggested that the co-occurrence of autism and intellectual disability might be as low as 41%, most research has found a co-occurrence rate of 68–80%. Most of these people have been found to have a mild to moderate intellectual disability, with fewer than 20% having a severe or profound intellectual disability. Autistic adults and children can also have epilepsy or similar neurological disorders, with level of intellectual (learning) disability possibly being an important factor in predicting whether epilepsy is present.

Understanding and Responding to Autism: The SPELL framework (2nd edition)
© Pavilion Publishing and Media Ltd and its licensors 2018.

Those on the spectrum can also have health problems, such as bowel and digestive conditions, skins conditions and allergies. There are a number of special diets and programmes of supplements that aim to account for some of these issues – the effect of gluten, casein (in dairy) and candida (yeast) are most commonly researched. It is not known how many people this affects.

Finally, there are some psychiatric disorders which can co-occur with autism; for some people, the anxiety they experience can develop to such a level as to be classified as a mental health condition in its own right. Often the signs of autism are misinterpreted as a mental disorder due to poor understanding of the condition. Some people, especially those with Asperger syndrome or high-functioning autism, can spend many years in the mental health system receiving inappropriate support, until they eventually receive an autism spectrum diagnosis. This is thought to be even more of an issue for women on the spectrum.

It is important to note that diagnosis of autism in the presence of co-occurring conditions is not always easy, especially between ADHD and autism as the symptoms of ADHD can often look like autism in some children and at certain ages. Sometimes it is necessary to wait until children are older to work out which is the primary diagnosis and it takes professionals familiar with both conditions to be able to discern the differences.

However, the important thing here is to recognise that autistic people can also have other conditions, many (but not all) of which may be treatable or may be alleviated by the correct approach to support (for example, anxiety). Those supporting autistic people should be wary of diagnostic overshadowing, i.e. staff and carers ignoring or underreporting additional issues because they see them as part of the autism and therefore not treatable. It is important to determine the cause of the problem if possible and whether this relates to autism or another factor.

Key learning point

- **It is important to recognise other conditions and offer treatment or help.**

Uneven profile of strengths and weaknesses

Most autistic people have an uneven or spiky profile of things they can and cannot do. On IQ tests, they may score very well on some domains but very poorly on others. An overall or full-scale IQ is often relatively meaningless for this population as it usually masks a very mixed profile. In autistic people, non-verbal or spatial skills (jigsaws, matching patterns etc) are normally higher than verbal skills.

This spiky profile can cause substantial misunderstandings, as people can see that an individual can do one (sometimes even more complex) activity but not do another often simpler one. This can lead people to think that the person is being difficult or lazy, choosing to only do what they want to do. However, this is rarely the case.

Exceptional skills

Some people can have very special skills, which are over and above what one would expect from their normal level of functioning. These are sometimes called 'islets of ability'. The man who can draw the Forth Bridge from any perspective is one example. This young man didn't speak and had real difficulty with day-to-day living skills, but had a special interest in numbers and could draw this complex structure from any perspective.

The artist Stephen Wiltshire is an example of what is sometimes called an 'autistic savant' – he can paint scenes after studying them for a relatively short period of time. He is most famous for his London landscapes. You can check out his website to see more about him and see some of his pictures. http://www.stephenwiltshire.co.uk/

Others may have gifts in music or mathematics. People often think that all autistic people have these types of special skills (Dustin Hoffman's portrayal of an autistic man in Rain Man may have played a part in this). However, it is believed that these people are relatively rare and that less than 10% of the autistic population have one of these extremely special skills. Many more will have strengths in one or more aspects of everyday functioning.

Understanding and Responding to Autism: The SPELL framework (2nd edition)

Autistic people often have the following strengths.

- Visual skills – this means that we can often use visual means to communicate where verbal means have failed.

- Highly knowledgeable about areas of special interest – this can be used to help find routes to motivation and involvement.

- Systemising – they are good at making sense of the logical or concrete (scientific strengths).

- Visual memory and factual memory skills.

- Focus on repetition – autistic people are often very good at repetitive tasks, taking care in what they do; they can maintain attention and motivation in these types of tasks for much longer.

- Precision and accuracy – autistic people like things to be precise and accurate; this means that they are often able to do their own quality control!

It has been said by commentators that the world needs autistic people – for example, Temple Grandin and later Wendy Lawson, both on the autism spectrum themselves, commented that 'without autistic people NASA couldn't operate'. This could probably also be said of Apple, Microsoft and many universities' science, electronics and computing departments!

Example

I recently heard about an autistic man who went to a hospital for an interview for a job as a porter. When the surgeon learnt about him, he insisted he wanted him to work in his operating theatre, cleaning and arranging his equipment.

Key learning points

- **Just like everyone else, people on the autism spectrum have strengths as well as difficulties.**

- **However the difficulties do exist and it is not helpful to ignore them.**

- **It is important to play to people's strengths.**

Underlying mechanisms

'In order to understand a person, you must understand what that person understands.'
(Sören Kierkegaard)

This quote neatly encapsulates the essence of working with autistic people – and everyone else. We are indebted to Swedish Psychiatrist Dr Lena Nylander for its use.

Important to understanding autistic people is the understanding of what is sometimes referred to as 'autistic intelligence'. We have already mentioned the issue of the spiky IQ profile in children and autistic adults and the fact that IQ tests based on verbal reasoning discriminate against them. For example, for a true measure of IQ it is often considered better to use a non-verbal test such as the Raven's Progressive Matrices rather than one requiring verbal skills such as the Weschler Intelligence Scale for Children (WISC).

However, potentially more important is understanding 'autistic thinking'.

There are a number of mechanisms that have been proposed to help understand autism. These include:

- theory of mind/mind blindness

- executive function/dysfunction

- central coherence weakness.

Theory of mind/mind blindness

Theory of mind has been defined as 'the ability to understand what other people think, believe, feel and to predict behaviour on the basis of those thoughts, beliefs, feelings' (Premack & Woodruff, 1978). It is something that we learn to do at a very early stage and it is thought to be fully developed by the time we are five years old. It doesn't emerge all at once but develops over the course of the first four to five years of life. There are a number of precursors to a fully developed theory of mind, which start to develop from about nine months of age:

- Following others' gaze.

- Using eye contact to share information, get others' attention etc.

- Pretend play – usually starts to emerge at about 18 months of age.

Understanding and Responding to Autism: The SPELL framework (2nd edition)
© Pavilion Publishing and Media Ltd and its licensors 2018.

- Teasing.

- Joking.

- Deception and lying.

- Understanding where knowledge comes from (i.e. that you have to see, hear or be told something in order to know it).

- Understanding beliefs (i.e. that other people may hold beliefs that are different to your own).

The final stage, which indicates a fully developed theory of mind, is understanding what is called 'false belief'. This is when we understand that the belief someone did have is not now true because something has changed. For example, the famous Sally-Anne story (a psychological test) in which Sally leaves the room having put her marble in her basket and when she is out of the room naughty Anne moves the marble and puts it in a box. At this point Sally has a false belief that the marble is still in the basket where she left it as she is not privy to the knowledge that Anne has moved it – i.e. Sally has a false belief as to the location of the marble. When she comes back inside to get her marble she will look in her basket as that is where she believes it to be.

We know that autistic children have great difficulties with all levels of theory of mind and, although may sometimes develop some pretend play or the ability for deception or playing jokes, it is usually much later than their peers and often not as intuitive or natural. In 1985, Simon Baron-Cohen, Alan Leslie and Uta Frith showed that when tested on false belief using the Sally-Anne task, 80% of children on the autism spectrum fail the test. In contrast, 80% of those without autism but with an intellectual disability passed the test. These findings have been replicated many times. Some autistic people can learn to pass these tests but may still not be able to use theory of mind in a natural situation to understand why people do what they do.

This difficulty contributes to why autistic people find other people unpredictable and interactions stressful.

Importance of the eyes

The theory of mind hypothesis has been developed over time with some more recent work looking at the importance of the eyes as 'windows to the mind'. Our eyes can tell us a lot about what people are looking at, thinking, feeling, wanting etc but we know that autistic people appear to be blind to the importance of the eyes. In fact, many autistic people report that they cannot even look into people's eyes because what they see scares them or makes them very uncomfortable.

‘ I don't know how people see so much in each other's eyes, all I see is jelly. ’

Joe Powell

This is another example of a test for theory of mind and in particular of whether a child or adult can understand the significance of the eyes. The question is: which candy does Charlie want?

Figure 5: Theory of mind test

The autistic person will usually choose the candy they themselves prefer, assuming Charlie will choose the same, irrespective of where his eyes are looking. This test illustrates the difficulty such subjects have in 'reading' facial expression or eye gaze.

It is important to note that not all autistic people will have problems in this area, making it an unreliable diagnostic marker.

So, in summary:

- Autistic people have difficulties in attributing mental states to others – 'mind reading'. This is also seen in their difficulty in reading facial expressions and gesture.

- They are generally good at following rules and systems but not at understanding events caused by human behaviour which is generally much more unpredictable for them and the cause of anxiety.

Impaired executive functioning

Executive functioning is a set of skills controlled by the front part of our brain (our frontal lobe) and is what we need to be able to plan ahead, organise things and deal with sequences of actions and thoughts etc. Executive functioning is:

- needed to help us pay attention and to plan ahead

- needed when a change of plan occurs – when routine behaviour is no longer enough

- crucial for keeping several tasks going at the same time and for switching between them (multi-tasking)

- crucial for what are called 'high level' decisions between two or more conflicting responses.

It is also what we need for behavioural control. For example, it is essential for overriding automatic behaviour and inhibiting inappropriate impulsive actions. Executive functioning is what stops us shouting out in the supermarket, 'Gosh, isn't that woman very tall!', even when that is what we might be thinking. It is what allows us to pay attention when someone is talking to us, even when something else is going on in the background. It is what allows us to plan for what might happen later or tomorrow or next year. It is what helps us to cope when something unexpected happens and when our original plan no longer works. It is what allows us to do the ironing while talking on the telephone and keeping one ear on what the children are doing in the next room.

Executive function is like an inbuilt diary or compass, keeping us on time and on track.

Impaired executive functioning is most commonly seen in people who have had brain damage to the area at the front of their brain called the frontal lobes. Almost all of those on the autism spectrum, as well as those with other conditions such as ADHD and dyspraxia, show problems with executive functioning.

Without intact executive functioning we see difficulties such as:

- problems with following sequences

- problems organising and planning ahead

- problems with overriding automatic responses and inhibiting inappropriate actions – this can show in very direct responses, inability to tell lies, what can appear as inappropriate statements

- problems being able to shift from one task to another

- lack of flexibility which results in resistance to change

- 'shutdown' – when people can take no more information or stimulation.

Weak central coherence

Central coherence helps us to differentiate the most salient information from all the information available to us. It also helps us to understand cause and effect and to generalise information learnt in one context to another.

It is what we are using when we use context to help us understand something; we piece together parts of something to make a whole or we remember the gist of a message rather than the detail. Autistic people have what is called 'weak central coherence'. They usually have problems linking parts to make a whole. When they do a jigsaw puzzle they often do not use the picture to help them – some autistic people do jigsaw puzzles upside down because they are using the geometric shape of the pieces rather than the picture to help them do it. When they recognise faces they may be recognising you by your eyes, nose, earrings or lipstick, rather than your face as a whole. As such, they can become very confused when someone shares that same feature with you. Similarly, they can be confused in a very busy environment and find it difficult to identify the people they should go to for help, for example the day-care staff in a nursery. Even after quite a long time, they might still not appear to easily recognise the staff they see every day and often are helped by staff wearing a uniform (one item that makes them distinct from others in the environment, a detail that allows the child to recognise them as someone they can ask for help).

Some people can find it difficult to recognise people they have known for a very long time when they have simply changed their hairstyle. They may know intellectually that it is the same person, but their senses appear to be telling them something different.

Understanding and Responding to Autism: The SPELL framework (2nd edition)
© Pavilion Publishing and Media Ltd and its licensors 2018.

For example, a 5-year-old boy was rather unsettled in school one day, asking where his teacher was. It turned out the teacher had an important meeting to go to at lunchtime and had worn her long hair up in a bun rather than down around her shoulders as normal. It was only after lunch when she came back into class with her hair down that her young pupil said hello to her, apparently glad to see the teacher he recognized back again.

Quite often autistic people also have difficulty remembering the gist of a message or story and will often try and relay all the details, while at the same time perhaps missing the point. They often have difficulty understanding cause and effect – working out why something happened the way it happened. In general, they are strong on 'detail' but weaker on 'story' or getting the 'big picture'.

Finally, they often have difficulties generalising something they have learnt in one setting to another setting.

Example

One rather extreme example that a colleague told me about was a young man on the autism spectrum who rarely left his room as he appeared completely unable to walk down the stairs – he was so anxious about doing so. My colleague worked with him for a long time until the point he could come down the stairs in his house. However, they noted that he was still unable to come down the stairs anywhere else. This left them puzzled until they went on holidays and when they came back staff had painted the wall in the hallway from the original green colour to a blue. They noticed that the man could no longer come down his stairs at home. It appeared that he was so context dependent that he could only go down stairs if they had a green wall.

Peter Vermeulen calls this phenomenon 'context blindness'. Very few things in life have only one exact meaning – sometimes words, signs, facial expressions mean different things in different contexts. For example, when you see someone crying you immediately think they are sad, unless they are sitting in a theatre with their favourite comedian on stage, then they are more likely to be crying with laughter.

Peter Vermeulen reminds us that this issue with context can cause substantial difficulties, not least if people develop inaccurate scripts for conversations and actions. For example, a young man goes into the supermarket and the girl on the till smiles at him and wishes him a good weekend as he pays for the shopping. The young man thinks, 'she is smiling and being nice to me, she must like me, she must want to go on a date with me' and he says to the young girl, 'Will you be my girlfriend?'.

For most of us, central coherence is an automatic activity. Items that are held together/connected in meaning are easier to process. It can also be a limitation in that it stops us processing information that doesn't make sense; having weak central coherence gives children and autistic adults many of their skills. They can often do well on tests of block design (building a design from blocks so that one side of the blocks matches a picture) and embedded figures (where an image is hidden in a very complex, usually colourful, repeating pattern). They can have excellent rote memory and as noted above can be very good at jigsaws without using the pictures. Tests that require you to ignore context and process detail are easier for autistic children and adults.

So, in summary, weak central coherence results in:

- problems linking parts to make a whole

- good on detail – weak on big picture

- difficulty in understanding cause and effect

- difficulty in generalising what has been learnt in one situation to another

- difficulty in knowing where to focus attention

- literal understanding of language.

Exercise 5: Getting the message

Part 1

Imagine you are running a meeting and a secretary comes in to give you a message that one of your colleagues has phoned. The message they have received is as follows:

'There has been an enormous accident on the road up ahead. There are 5 or 6 cars all badly damaged. There is a red Volkswagen upside down and a yellow Skoda has crossed the central reservation. I can see three fire engines and there are 4 ambulances at the minute. Lots of police cars and I can hear the air ambulance arriving. I don't know how long it is going to take to clear but am not going anywhere at the minute.'

Understanding and Responding to Autism: The SPELL framework (2nd edition)
© Pavilion Publishing and Media Ltd and its licensors 2018.

What information is your secretary mostly likely to give you?

Part 1 answers

Part 2

For the following paragraph, try to rewrite it with just the most important information that the person being spoken to needs to have in order to understand what is going to happen during the rest of the day? Which elements might be more difficult to translate for someone who is on the autism spectrum who doesn't process verbal information so easily? Can you think of how you might make this easier for the person?

'At 3pm we will catch the train to Margate. We will go for a swim, build sand castles and then have fish and chips. If the weather is bad we might go see your aunt or we will go to the museum and eat in the cafe.'

Part 2 answers

See Annex 5 for our responses to Exercise 5.

Key learning points

- **There are differences in how autistic people think and experience the world around them.**

- **Those on the autism spectrum have difficulties understanding mental states including emotions, which can mean the world around them is confusing and unpredictable.**

- **They have difficulty generalising information to different situations and contexts.**

- **They have difficulty processing sequences and too many sources of information at once.**

- **They tend to say what they see and think. They are direct; rarely intentionally rude.**

- **They often focus on the detail and find it difficult to see the bigger picture (which can be both a strength and a weakness).**

Stress and anxiety

Research has shown that autistic children and adults are more stressed and anxious than their neurotypical counterparts. Research has also found that autistic people show what is called higher residual levels of stress. When most of us are in a stressful situation our body responds by releasing a hormone called cortisol which helps us to remain in a state of arousal to deal with the stress. Once the stressful situation passes, our cortisol levels reduce again. However, in autistic people the cortisol levels do not reduce as much or as quickly. This means that each stressor (which may be something that seems very small to us) adds to the level of arousal until the person is eventually in 'meltdown'. Meltdown is not

Understanding and Responding to Autism: The SPELL framework (2nd edition)
© Pavilion Publishing and Media Ltd and its licensors 2018.

the same as having a temper tantrum – in the latter the child is trying to gain control. Meltdown is a sign of complete lack of control and ability to cope. A child or an adult in this state is usually in desperate need of help.

High levels of stress and anxiety are usually associated with reduced self-efficacy – it impairs our ability to be productive and cope in a range of other situations. Autistic people report that it is the most debilitating aspect of the condition.

We know that stress is reduced by:

- structure and predictability – for example, clear rules and an easy to navigate environment avoiding toxic sensory environments or over arousal – talking to someone in this state is usually the worst thing we can do

- increasing the level of control the person has by increasing choice making.

We will talk more about these strategies in Part 2.

Personal experiences

Personal accounts of autistic people

There are many books and websites and videos which help you to understand the personal experiences of people on the autism spectrum. Three of our favourites include:

- *My Autism and Me* (https://www.youtube.com/watch?v=ejpWWP1HNGQ)

- *Now't So Queer as Folk* with Jo Powell (http://www.youtube.com/watch?v=8BD-OviKW3s)

- Dean Beadle's talk to the NAS professional conference in 2013 (http://www.youtube.com/watch?v=LC0JytWaQZM).

These three videos show different sides of autism, illustrate some of the gender differences and remind us that everyone is an individual.

Family experiences

There are a number of issues that are faced by families of children on the autism spectrum. Some of the issues might be different when their children are grown up, but there will still be difficulties. The list of issues below come from an account written by Gabriels and Hill in the US almost 20 years ago. As you read them, think about how it compares to the situation now, where you live.

Diagnostic confusion – sometimes it takes a long time to get a diagnosis and it needs to be made by a specifically trained professional. Even once they have a diagnosis they don't necessarily get the information, support or intervention needed. Many adults receive a diagnosis of autism after already having several other diagnoses.

Uneven and unusual course of development – because autistic children can often have 'good' skills in one or more areas, people often find it difficult to accept that they can be so severely affected in other areas, resulting in a lack of understanding about how to support the child.

Attractive appearance – autistic children, in particular, can often look more attractive than a typically developing child and because autism is an invisible disability, the public are not very understanding of the difficulties parents are facing.

Behaviour in public – this can often be very difficult to deal with and because of the invisibility of the condition, parents often feel they are being judged by others around them as their child gets over-stimulated or very 'demanding' in the supermarket.

Professional 'turfism' – parents often report that there are many professionals involved in just one child's case, each one claiming responsibility for a different aspect and not necessarily working together.

Fads and unproven theories – the internet has opened up a world of possibilities for parents in terms of obtaining information that professionals don't always pass on to them. However, this also has the downside that people publish information on a range of fads and unproven theories that can confuse and sometimes even trick parents into signing up for interventions that have no research evidence supporting them.

Psychological impacts on families – many families experience guilt about their son/daughter having autism. There is also often much stress created by difficulties trying to find appropriate services. Older families may worry about what will happen to their son or daughter once they are too frail to support them.

More recently, a study by Research Autism, the Institute of Psychiatry and the Institute of Education on research priorities in the UK (*A Future Made Together,*

Understanding and Responding to Autism: The SPELL framework (2nd edition)
© Pavilion Publishing and Media Ltd and its licensors 2018.

published 2013), found that *fear of or for the future* was a major factor for families. Parents expressed real anxiety at what would happen to their children when they were no longer able to support them. This related to those across the whole spectrum – those with associated intellectual disabilities and those without ID.

Another issue that can have a substantial effect on the family is the difficulties children (and adults) can have with sleeping. While this has a direct effect on the child themselves, it also has an effect on other members of the family.

Key learning points

- **Despite increased awareness, life for families has not changed much.**
- **The eternal question – 'what happens after I'm gone?' – is as relevant today as it ever has been.**

Sibling experiences

It is important not to forget other children in the family – the impact of having an autistic sibling can be enormous and variable. Often siblings have to act as young carers to support their parents. There is very little sibling support available, although most siblings I have spoken to do not want special groups etc. They express that what they need is support for their parents, some skilled respite, so that parents can spend time with their other children. Many siblings may well have their own specific needs too – the conditions in the syndrome mix often affect the other children in a family too.

It is also important not to forget the autistic person's experience of their neurotypical sibling. Watching their sibling go off to university, have relationships, get their first job, can be very difficult for young autistic people to deal with.

Example: Katy's experience of having an autistic brother.

- *'Although he can be annoying, he does not tease me or annoy me the way I have heard other people my age with siblings of roughly the same age gap complaining of.'*
- *'He likes to play with me, although his timing could be better, for example if he wants to have a water fight when I'm in the middle of doing my homework, this can be slightly problematic.'*
- *'One negative is the way people look at us (me, him, Mum and Dad) in the street, or shop, if he breaks down (which doesn't happen often, but still...) or if he is wearing his headphones, or walks or talks in a way which we find normal, but other people find strange.'*

- *'A question I am commonly asked by other children is, "You know your brother? No offence, but what's wrong with him?" People are generally not very aware of autism, and when you say "disability" to people – certainly children anyway – they immediately think 'wheelchair' and very few even think about other disabilities besides physical. It just makes me wonder if something could be done to raise awareness?'*

- *'I do not invite friends round as much as I would like; this is not really anyone's fault, but it is still quite annoying and awkward and made it very hard to make new friends when I moved to my secondary school, although I can have my friends round who I have known since I was about three or four, as my brother knows them quite well.'*

- *'He keeps me awake a lot of the time, making me very tired and late for school the next day, and he also "nerdles" (non-verbal vocalisation) a lot.'*

- *'He says embarrassing stuff about me to my friends.'*

- *'He is at least as good as me in some aspects of biology, maths and history (he is 10 and I'm 13 – set 1 science and maths), but because many people think autism is a learning disability….until recently his school was trying to make him do his number bonds to 10 which he didn't want to do because he was bored of them. I think this is a shame, as he just needs to be asked in the right way.'*

- *'When he gets really worked up, if he starts panicking, he will sometimes just lose all his words. If this happens, he will try to find another way to tell us that he is panicking. This can be a problem – once him, Mum, my godmother and me were in a restaurant in France. Looking back, it was a very crowded room, everyone was speaking French, and he thought we were going to have a picnic (this was the original plan, so it was what he had in his head). After a while, there was a baby crying, and this just seemed to push him over the edge. He had had a way of saying, 'Help get me out of here before I hurt someone', which was just to quickly pinch the nearest person once on the arm, but someone at school had told him (probably with the best will in the world) that only naughty boys pinch, so he lost his way of communicating panic. So when the baby started crying, he knocked over a wine glass (me and Mum later worked out that he had seen this happen on TV, and the person who knocked the glass over was carried out). When we still stayed in the restaurant, he eventually threw a fork at the table with the baby, so Mum got him out. The lesson from this story: if he gets worked up, the key thing is to calm him down, not tell him off.*

  He looks for a solution to the problem, but does not think through the consequences the way we do (for an extreme example read Gone by Michael Grant – it's a good book).'

> ■ 'He can't have too much noise going on at once as it hurts his ears. This is a pain for me as I play five instruments to varying standards, and I also listen to a lot of music. It also means that when I do manage to have friends round, we have to be fairly quiet.'
>
> ■ 'Mum and Dad have to devote a lot of their time and attention to my brother. I have grown up with this, so it isn't much of a problem; I don't really notice it most of the time. This is extremely frustrating, but understandable, as Mum can't help me with my homework or music practice, or whatever, if he is trying to climb out of a window. Mum spends a lot of her time arguing either with, or for, him.
>
> ■ If Dad is at work and Mum is working on an essay or something, then I will sometimes have to help look after him; I do not mind this in itself, because as I have said, he likes playing with me, but it gets in the way of homework and stuff I want to be doing.'

Summary of Part 1

- Neurodiversity extends across the population.
- For a diagnosis of autism core features must be present but each person will be unique.
- Autism comes with many strengths but the nature of the difficulties can make people very vulnerable.
- Individualisation of approaches based on the person's needs is very important.
- Approaches used should be inclusive – what is good for autistic people is good for everyone.

Now go through the quiz you completed at the beginning again (**Annex 1**). See if you find it any easier to answer the questions and check your answers against the crib sheet in **Annex 2**.

Introduction to helpful approaches to support

The SPELL framework provides a context for other approaches and a way of organising help through the environment and interactions. It is a socially valid mechanism for understanding and responding to autism:

- **Structure:** we all need structure in our lives to organise and predict future events.
- **Positive approaches and expectations:** we all need to be seen positively, valued and allowed to pursue our interests and supported to achieve our potential.

- **Empathy:** we all need other people to have empathy for our point of view and vice versa.

- **Low arousal:** we all need to reduce unhealthy, stress and confrontation in our lives and enjoy peaceful times.

- **Links:** we all need to be treated fairly and consistently and have help with any problems.

We now move onto Part 2 of this workbook, which goes on to describe the SPELL framework and explain each element of the framework in detail.

Understanding and Responding to Autism: The SPELL framework (2nd edition)
© Pavilion Publishing and Media Ltd and its licensors 2018.

Part 2: Supporting children and adults on the autism spectrum

The SPELL framework

This section will explore the SPELL framework in detail. It is important to note that the framework has been developed by The National Autistic Society in its schools and adult services through evidence-based practice since 1964. It is not an intervention or an approach as such, but a framework for the development of understanding and good practice. It provides a context for other approaches and interventions, underpinning person-centred approaches for people on the autism spectrum. In addition, the framework has been developed dynamically, building on input from autistic people themselves, their families and professionals, and the changing narrative and climate around autism.

The overall aim of the framework is to improve our understanding of the nature of autism and with it maximise opportunities for children and adults on the autism spectrum.

The SPELL framework is based on five key values or principles.

1. It is **individual** – each child or adult on the autism spectrum is different. Interventions and support must be individual and centred around that person. The framework is consistent with the drive for person-centred approaches more widely.

2. It is **hopeful** – there is a positive emphasis on what can be achieved rather than dwelling on what cannot. It is based on the idea that people can develop and learn, and that we can make a difference to their quality of life. It focuses on strengths and uses what we know about autism to help people to compensate for the difficulties.

3. It is **honest** – it avoids exaggerated or misleading claims, and teaches people to admit that they might not have all the answers and that they might need to work with others to find the best way forward for those they are supporting.

It works on the basis of effective, open relationships and communication – listening to others, particularly autistic people. It is an open-minded but cautious approach to interventions.

4. It is **respectful** – it acknowledges the right of the individual to be different but also recognises that the individual may need our understanding, help and support and offers that support in a way that is acceptable to each person. It aims to minimise the disabling effects of the condition.

5. It is **ethical** – interventions are based on thorough assessment and on the principles of:

■ 'least restrictive' approach and equality of opportunity

■ no use of aversive, hazardous or painful techniques

■ positive practices actively promoted

■ doing no harm

■ not promoting potentially harmful or untested theories

■ interventions being socially valid – accepted by, and which aid inclusion in, the wider community.

There are three main goals of intervention in autism. First, interventions should aim to increase opportunity. Second, interventions should aim to understand the context and need for what may be seen as problematic behaviours, especially those that impact on the quality of life for the individual and reduce the respect received by others. Finally, interventions should aim to improve or enhance the quality of life of the individual.

The framework involves respect for different behaviours and ways of seeing the world. However, it does not agree with leaving individuals to their own devices without help or support, and recognises that for many autistic people life can be difficult.

In addition to these key goals, intervention should be tailored to the needs of the individual and should recognise the features of autism such as the need to reduce anxiety or uncertainty or sensory processing difficulties.

It is also important to treat any other conditions that the person may have (for example, allergies, epilepsy etc).

Finally, the framework works with the strengths and skills the person has or wishes to develop. It is not a deficit model focused only on problems. It is based on developing a thorough knowledge and understanding of the individual and building a relationship and a rapport with them.

Understanding and Responding to Autism: The SPELL framework (2nd edition)
© Pavilion Publishing and Media Ltd and its licensors 2018.

To do this, people have to be committed to making life better for that individual on that person's terms – only then can we help people to move forward in their lives. This rapport, commitment, the development of a relationship with the person and persistence to achieve are essential to the implementation of personalised approaches.

There are five core elements to the framework:

- Structure.
- Positive.
- Empathy.
- Low arousal.
- Links.

We are going to look at each of these elements in turn. As we cover each we will look at examples of how that principle can be implemented. For each element we will look at examples of violation (when people do things that ignore or openly oppose the SPELL principle – please note that violation refers to the principle, not the person), misunderstanding (when the principle is mis-applied due to lack of understanding of the principle) and good practice (where what people do complies with the principle and shows good understanding). **Figure 6** summarises this.

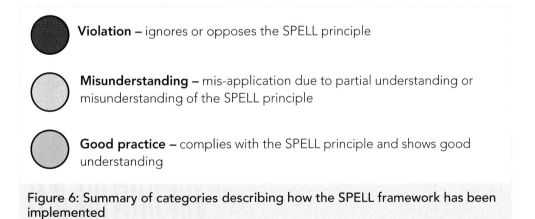

Violation – ignores or opposes the SPELL principle

Misunderstanding – mis-application due to partial understanding or misunderstanding of the SPELL principle

Good practice – complies with the SPELL principle and shows good understanding

Figure 6: Summary of categories describing how the SPELL framework has been implemented

It is important to recognise that what we are aiming for is autism-friendliness but with the acknowledgement that not all people will react in the same way to approaches or difficult situations.

Structure

We all need structure and order in our lives. Some of us need it more than others, depending on our own strengths and weaknesses, how busy our lives are and how many things we have to co-ordinate. Structure helps us to make sense of the world and therefore it helps to reduce our anxiety and to be calm and confident. It helps us to take part in activities, make choices and learn and it makes us less dependent on others.

Structure helps us to feel in control and to organize our lives effectively and to achieve goals, whether they are small day-to-day goals or longer term to do with lifestyle or work.

Thinking activity

Think of some of the things that you use to provide structure and predictability in your lives (for example, most of us use a diary of some sort).

Answers

When thinking about supporting autistic people, we need to think about structure in the environment, routines and programmes, the presentation of tasks and activities and our own approach (e.g. how we communicate).

Structure is the cornerstone of all good autism-specific approaches and it enjoys good social validity, helping people to take control of their lives and make choices. Feeling good about accomplishing a task or a goal or being in control of our lives is good for our mental health.

Exercise 6

In the space below, write down the steps you go through on an average morning between waking up and going out the door to work or college.

Now think about the following questions:

■ How would you feel and what would happen if you couldn't do the third step that you outlined?

  ■ Would you be going to work in your pyjamas?

  ■ Would your kids be missing school and staying in bed all day?

  ■ Would you be feeling uncomfortable because you didn't get your shower?

  ■ Would you be feeling a bit grumpy because you hadn't had your first coffee?

■ Does your routine ever change? If so, in what circumstances? For example, when you are on holiday, when you have to attend training instead of going to work for your normal office hours etc.

■ What happens in your environment to prompt different parts of your routine (working on the assumption that you are not just a robot in the morning, in automatic mode!)? Some of the things that provide you with the cues for what to do next might include your alarm clock, your dog licking you and so on.

Usually we have some say about our routine – we have some degree of choice. Many children and adults on the autism spectrum may live in a world where routine is imposed on them by others. Sometimes this is a structure that has been carefully negotiated based on knowledge of what the individual prefers, but more often than not it is someone's misunderstanding of what the person needs. We'll come back to this shortly.

Exercise 7

Make a list of some of the examples of structure that you have come across being used with autistic children and adults. See if you can recognise any of these as you read through the examples provided in this section.

Structure makes the world more predictable; it plays to visual strengths and works on the level of the concrete rather than the abstract, which autistic people may have difficulties with. Autistic people may also have problems with sequencing or planning ahead; as with everyone, using structure can help to overcome these problems and speed up processing information such as requests or instructions. Finally, it also helps to reduce anxiety and improve self-efficacy and self-esteem.

It is important to remember that structure should be personalised, based on the needs of the individual. It will look different for different people. For example, routines should be based on the needs and preferences of the individual rather than a service-led regime. As people get older the type of structure that is helpful to them may change. It is here that the greatest care should be taken; even when using personalised approaches there is a risk of imposing unhelpful structure if the needs the person are not understood.

Structure is helpful for everyone; parents and carers advise that it makes things clearer and less confusing and tasks such as preparation quicker. It helps all of us understand and provide more seamless/confident support to someone taking part in an activity.

Understanding and Responding to Autism: The SPELL framework (2nd edition)
© Pavilion Publishing and Media Ltd and its licensors 2018.

Examples of good practice of structure

- A schedule or programme that clearly depicts:
    - what will happen and when
    - where to get help or materials.
- Change is programmed into the schedule.
- Individual schedules – these might change as the child grows up or in different situations as necessary.

Structure can aid independence by helping people to take control of their lives and be able to do things with less prompting from staff, teachers, carers etc. It also reduces anxiety in that the day becomes much more predictable and, as with everyone, visual reminders such as written instructions or pictures are useful so there is something visual to refer back to if we forget what is going to happen.

Having planned activities helps people to learn and develop. If you feel that a programme is in need of a change then planning that change is important and if handled well can enhance flexibility. For example, rather than visiting the same supermarket at the same time each week, perhaps try a different supermarket at the same time each week – and then vary that. The important thing is that change is **planned and communicated** not suddenly presented without warning. By being flexible we are helping to avoid the stress of change when well established routines are disrupted.

Another example is having a 'surprise' time on a daily schedule, for example the person is prepared for change by getting used to the idea that a surprise will occur – and will get to know that someone is going to ask them to do something they don't know about – it might just be asking them a question, or talking for five minutes about a topic, or watching a different video. This helps children and adults, who are rigid in their routines to the point that their opportunities are restricted, to be a little more flexible. It is important to note that this rigidity might be as much a result of a history of inappropriate or institutional settings as of the autism. Where this is related to trauma or severe anxiety, or where there is any uncertainty, the advice of a psychologist or psychiatrist should be sought.

Example: John

'When John first came to us he needed objects of reference. He was very anxious and he wasn't aware of his environment and we realised very quickly that symbols were meaningless to him and the problem with using photographs was that he has some perceptual problems as well so he was finding it difficult to make out the photos. So, for locations around the school we used objects of reference and this increased over time. He then started to use a PECS (Picture Exchange Communication System) book with sensory toys as motivation to use it. He was a very visual learner so we could get him to request his reward activities (such as mushroom lights etc) and that's how we started interaction with him. Objects of reference were used to help him to find his way around the school, with photographs of people and his PECS book. We helped him to interact through making choices using photos of the toys. Then we were able to move on to photographs for locations around the school. He then sped up very quickly, almost like magic.'

Example: Bob

'Bob really needs structure – he carries around a visual timetable and a 'deal card' (Wally stickers) as he really needs help to keep his attention on tasks. He started with a PECS book and has now moved on. He now takes responsibility for his visual structure – he does his own timetable from the big one in the class. He was very anxious about when he was going home so he needed a visual calendar in his bedroom of Monday to Sunday which portrayed the routine for each day, for example:

- *Monday: taxi, school, taxi, home, dinner, sleep.*
- *Tuesday: taxi, school, taxi, home, dinner, sleep.*
- *Wednesday: taxi, school, taxi, home, dinner, sleep.*
- *Thursday: taxi, school, taxi, home, dinner, sleep.*
- *Friday: taxi, school, taxi, home, dinner, sleep.*
- *Saturday: home.*
- *Sunday: home.'*

Understanding and Responding to Autism: The SPELL framework (2nd edition)

Some example of deal cards used by children at school:

Example: Jamie

It was Jamie's first day at the activity centre. A member of staff was allocated to support him. The kitchen was clearly labelled so he could be independent and not have to keep asking – he easily found the juice. This helped him not to feel anxious.

Staff concentrated on chatting to him, finding out what he liked and disliked, what he might like to make, helping him feel comfortable and involving him in making his own photo cards etc for his storage boxes.

Example: Dan

'Dan needed a reward as he really wasn't motivated. There weren't any behavioural issues; he just didn't seem alert enough. Then we moved onto a visual timetable and because the written word is always under the symbol, that's how he learnt to read – not by conventional methods. His PECS book became massive – loads of symbols with words underneath. Staff gradually became aware that he was reading the words. Now he doesn't use PECS but he still has a visual timetable. He rarely uses a deal card – motivation can usually be done verbally now. Dan is nine now but still has huge language difficulties; he appears to have good language in social circumstances but has learnt social phrases etc which he uses. If he can't see something he can't answer a 'what' question – he still needs lots of visual learning – the here and now – he still needs those visual supports. He'll still have a topic board with symbols and written words with him so he can be clear what is happening. He'll use the topic board to write about it afterwards. Spoken word is transient but if he has a hook to hang it on (the visual support) then he does better.'

Examples of misunderstanding

- Everyone follows the same schedule or routine.
- Routines become fixed, regimented.
- Activities always follow the same pattern (no change programmed into schedule).
- No attempt to vary activities or programme.

Example: Sara

Sara comes home from school at 3.30pm each day. Her two housemates are at a different school and don't get home until 4.00pm. When Sara comes in she is encouraged to go to her room and change into casual clothes and then to watch some TV. She begins to get more and more agitated, rocking and hitting her head with her hand and, when asked, staff report that she is probably a bit hungry and that they are just waiting for the others to get home and then it will be time for a snack. At 4.00pm the others arrived and they all sit down at the table for a cup of tea, a biscuit and some fruit at 4.20pm.

This example of Sara's experience illustrates a misunderstanding of the principle of structure; having a routine may be good but it is clear that Sara needed a different routine to the other two housemates and perhaps would have benefitted from her snack as soon as she had come in from school. She was not given control or autonomy.

Example: Fred

The speech and language therapist had suggested that Fred needed visual supports to help him around the house.

Symbols were made to go on all of his bedroom cupboards and drawers to illustrate where things were so that he could be more independent in getting dressed, putting away his laundry etc. Initially, symbols were also put up on the kitchen cupboards but over time these had been removed by staff.

When asked why, staff explained that Fred now knew where everything was in the kitchen, could get his cup out when making a cup of tea etc. And besides, having symbols on the cupboards in the kitchen wasn't very homely.

In this example of Fred's experiences, staff misunderstood why the symbols had been recommended and also had misunderstood the needs of clients like Fred. For many autistic people, taking away their visual structure can be the equivalent of taking away a wheelchair from someone who cannot walk – completely disabling them and likely to result in extreme anxiety or 'challenging behaviour'.

Understanding and Responding to Autism: The SPELL framework (2nd edition)

Examples of violation

- No pre-planned activity.
- Environment is chaotic or disorganised.
- An absence of visual signs and schedules.
- Activity is dependent on unpredictable factors (for example, weather, availability of staff).
- Person becomes over-dependent on verbal prompts (due to lack of visual cues).
- Routines and structure used are those of staff or carers rather than those that are useful to the individual.

Exercise 8

Write down some examples where a lack of structure has caused problems in your experience.

The sorts of things you might have come across are represented in some of the pictures below – messy, chaotic environments with no use of visual structure; people being offered activities (or activities on their timetable) that then don't happen for some reason and no alternative is in place – it is essential to always have a plan B that the person can understand, should it be needed.

Examples of structure (and some examples of no structure)

This is an example of a fairly traditional TEACCH visual timetable. These children are quite young and most of them can only deal with three or four items on their timetable. The timetable is identified by the child's photo and written name. The children complete a task, remove the symbol, put it into the box at the bottom and then check what is next.

This is a much more complex visual timetable for older children/adolescents who can cope with lots of items.

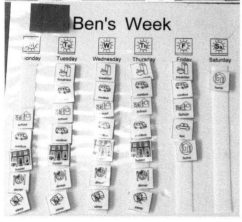

This is an example of a weekly timetable for a young man who needs to know what his whole week holds otherwise he becomes very anxious. It needs to have Saturday and Sunday on it with a symbol for 'home'. It includes the different types of transport he uses – minibus to get to the hostel after school, taxi to go home at the weekend etc. Without this, Ben finds it almost impossible to get through the day.

Understanding and Responding to Autism: The SPELL framework (2nd edition)
© Pavilion Publishing and Media Ltd and its licensors 2018.

This is an example of a one-to-one session. The child's work is presented on the left, while on the right there is a 'finished' tray where all materials go when they have been completed.

This is an example of an independent work session where the child has to complete a number of tasks independently and without assistance from the tutor.

The physical structure of the session and the concept of working from left to right that have been developed during one-to-one sessions, are essential tools that replace the tutor. The child immediately knows what to do, what to do when finished, where to go and what happens next.

This is a good example of using structure in the environment to make it clear what the purpose of the session is. All the other musical instruments are in the cupboards and the chairs are arranged around the visual supports that tell the children which three instruments they are going to play today. The layout of the chairs means that the children go straight to them and sit down, without getting distracted.

For many autistic children, knowing what is for dinner is quite important.

Notice how all the symbols include both words and pictures. Notice how the pictures are very clearly of the things the children will have available to eat that day. The different elements of the meal are presented separately with as little context as possible. This avoids children expecting food to be arranged on the plate in a particular order.

This is a wonderful example of structure to help this child become more independent, not only at making his snack but also at making choices. The way the items are laid out guides the child through the steps and reduces the need for staff prompts.

This is a storage system used in a school for autistic children; this is in a class of older children. Each drawer is labelled for a subject and within each drawer each child has a folder with their photo and name on it so they can easily identify their folder and put their work away.

An example of a work folder that would then be filed in the storage system above.

For some children it would be necessary to colour code the drawers and files etc but in this class this wasn't necessary.

Understanding and Responding to Autism: The SPELL framework (2nd edition)
© Pavilion Publishing and Media Ltd and its licensors 2018.

An example of a choice board. The young person can be guided to the board to choose a preferred activity for a 'choice' session on his timetable. He responds well to black on red background and so this is what has been used.

This is an example of a communication tool that would be used during a school day to prompt a child or communicate the next activity, such as playtime. It can be used to reduce the need for a verbal prompt. It is also used to help the child to request something. Note that these come from Malta and one version is in English and the other is in Maltese for a child who speaks Maltese.

These are two examples of visual structures. Andrew's visual timetable uses PECS symbols; Joshua's is written. Both children do their own timetable for the evening routine after they have come in from school.

Structure of the environment can also be important.

Having a clear route to the toilet with no distractions can be essential – here the screens guide the child to the door of the toilet making it much more likely that they will make it there with less prompting from adults.

This is an example of a 'good morning' routine for a man who needs some gentle reminders of what to do when he arrives at his gardening project each day. This includes practical things such as taking off his coat and also social things such as saying good morning.

There can be no doubt as to what is in this cupboard.

Here the cupboards are clearly labelled and the kitchen is well laid out, free from chaos yet homely. Photographs of what is actually inside each cupboard are used – this avoids any difficulty with literal understanding and can easily be redone if the content of the cupboards has to change for any reason.

This and the next photo illustrate a structured system to help people sort screws in a woodwork workshop. The screws are put in the white box nearest the camera and then the person can match them to one of the various sizes and put them in the appropriate box. They can match by colour or by the screw size. There is a video of a member of staff showing how this is used.

Understanding and Responding to Autism: The SPELL framework (2nd edition)
© Pavilion Publishing and Media Ltd and its licensors 2018.

Once the screws have been sorted using the system above, they can be taken to the boxes on the shelves, which use the same labelling system. In the instruction for each item that is made at the workshop, the screws needed are identified both by size and by colour.

This is a shadow board. The saw on the top left is in use – so you can see the 'shadow'. This allows the people working in the workshop to return tools to the board with minimal help. It also makes it much easier to find the tools than if they were in a big toolbox or drawer. You can see this shadow board being used in the film **Andrew tidies up the workshop**.

This is a visual structure for someone who finds waiting difficult. It has some of the most important prompts needed for this person at the top and then it has space for a timetable (nearest the camera). This is only A4 size and folds up so that it can be carried discreetly in a bag or pocket for use in the shops, cafe etc.

Each room in this centre has a different coloured label on the door. These colours are used throughout the centre in the signposting to help people move around as independently as possible.

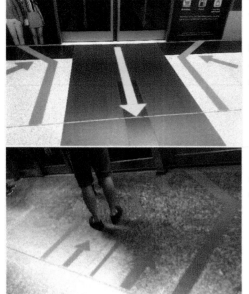

An example of social validity. Here clear markings illustrate where you should stand if you are waiting to board the train and where people will walk when getting off the train.

Here the visual structure helps people to queue in a more orderly manner while waiting to board the train.

Watch the film **Debbie and Daniel** (all video clips are available to download from https://www.pavpub.com/understanding-and-responding-to-autism-self-study-resources/). This is rather old now but is powerful in explaining how easily structure can be introduced and how effective it can be. It can make life so much better for both the child and the family or carers. The second part looks at how structure can also help to support choice-making skills. Pay attention to what she says and see if you can pick up an illustration of the hopefulness in her approach.

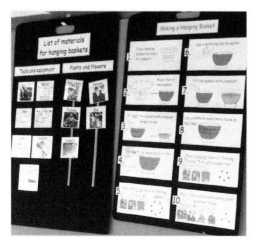

These boards show the equipment needed and the stages to go through to prepare a hanging basket at a garden project. These are especially important for new people and even the regular workers at the project are sometimes seen to check them if they have forgotten the next stage.

Another activity to support visual structure – here the table is prepared for laminating (and the one beside it for shredding). There are photos showing the various stages and the tables are set out to help people move from one step to the next.

IPads, smart phones and so on are a portable way of taking your visual structure with you. Here a young man is checking his diary to see how many days are left until the concert he is looking forward to.

Here a young man is cooking soup independently using photos and a clear written instruction on his iPad that he swipes as he completes each part of the task.

In these two photos, the structure is primarily in the way the room is organised. You can see how there is the sofa and TV and games corner, primarily for breaks.

There is a work desk, book stand, Lego table and computer desk. For each different task, the child works at a different station. You can also see his visual timetable on the board etc.

Watch the video **Using visual structure to promote independence**. This shows a young man at school in Norway using visual structure to help him independently pack his bag at the end of the day and get ready to go home.

Watch the video **Andrew tidies up the workshop**. In this short clip Andrew puts away all the materials and equipment with just a verbal prompt from the staff. The clearly structured environment means that it is easy for him to find where everything goes. You can see Andrew using the shadow board featured in the photos.

This is an example of structure used to store information at college so that students can easily find their work files, their post etc without support from staff and therefore aiding independence.

Understanding and Responding to Autism: The SPELL framework (2nd edition)
© Pavilion Publishing and Media Ltd and its licensors 2018.

Paddington station – not somewhere one normally thinks of as a good place for an autistic person to work! However, this is where Joe works. Within his kiosk, the world is quite focused.

People queue up, usually in quite an orderly fashion, and he deals with people one by one. If someone gets annoyed or abusive Joe has permission to close his window until they go away. He has a script, the environment is free from distractions and, as with all staff, he has regular breaks.

This is clearly not a good example of an autism-friendly environment. There is very little structure; it looks like the person is just cutting up pieces of paper, perhaps to make pictures.

It isn't an adult activity and there is chaos in the background. In addition, the table is too low for this person to work at.

This is the board that used to be home to the visual timetable and pictures of staff on duty, until support staff stopped using it.

We do have to be careful not to impose our own ideas of structure; it is important to know the individual in order to judge what useful structure would be. What may look like chaos to some of us might include important structure to the autistic child, with everything in its perfect place. Before starting to introduce structure, it is important to understand the person and what structure already exists for them.

The importance of structure may be underestimated for the people described as more able. This is a common mistake, especially if the person appears confident and has good language skills.

Underlying problems with understanding other people in context or in processing information may cause great personal anxiety. Masking of autism symptoms to appear 'competent' has been widely reported, especially by girls and women. We should reassure the person that everyone needs structure to survive the world. The person's self-confidence and self-esteem may suffer and they may seek constant clarification and reassurance or be deterred by fear of failure and uncertainty. Structure also helps with the formation of relationships by clarifying expectations and timescales and avoiding confrontation.

Watch the video **Supporting Jacob** to hear about the importance of structure for Jacob.

Joe Powell, a man with Asperger syndrome, in a discussion with Richard Mills had this to say.

'Comfort in exactness'.

❝ Without structure in my life I have real problems in understanding what I am meant to be doing and other people's expectations of me. Knowing who to approach for help and when – knowing what to do and when to do it and whether or not I have done what is required. I find it hard to ask a person for help but if it is clear to me in written form I am OK with that. I feel comfortable when things are clear and where there is more certainty and predictability. This helps to avoid me having to ask all the time – as I sometimes forget the essence of what has been said to me I get worried that I might have missed the point. This also helps avoid criticism of me for doing things that I think I have been doing OK with – and confrontation with people. People think because I don't have learning difficulties and appear bright that my autism doesn't affect me much so expect better of me. In fact I am still for all intents and purposes autistic and share this feature with my fellow service users, it just means that I may not show it in as demonstrative fashion as someone with learning difficulties. Because it is often hard for me to understand or remember what other people really think or the context for social or work interactions I often become oversensitive to what they might be thinking. It is not that I don't care what they think or that I am oblivious – I am not – it is that I frequently think I think too much and care too much. Thoughts go round and round in my head. All of this can cause me to become anxious and progressively incapable of doing anything. ❞

In summary, structure is essential to an autism-friendly or autism-specific approach and a lack of structure signifies a lack of understanding of autism. A lack of structure is problematic to all of us but especially people who are more concrete or visual thinkers and less likely to be flexible. It is important to remember that this is an individualised approach and what works as structure for one person may not work for other people.

Scenario 1

Harry, Jim and John all attend the activity centre in the local town three days a week. They all travel together and when they come in from the centre, staff show them their visual timetable for the evening, which consists of the same activities for all three – snack, TV, craft activity, eating dinner, making a hot drink, TV, bath or shower, and bed.

Is this an example of good practice, misunderstanding or violation of the principle of structure?

(Answers for each scenario are provided in **Annex 9**.)

Positive approaches and expectations

Positive approaches and expectations are a key part of the framework affecting the narrative around the person and our expectations. We should be positive and optimistic and provide opportunity. Reduction of opportunity can be a self-fulfilling prophecy. Temple Grandin is professor of animal science at Colorado State University. She is also autistic. She lectures on animal science as well as autism. Her book *Emergence: Labelled autistic* (1986) was one of the first books written by an autistic person. Grandin emphasises the danger of leaving individuals entirely to their own devices: 'They must be prevented from simply shutting out the world'.

Positive approaches are about:

- not leaving the individual to their own devices

- sensitively and actively intervening to reduce any disabling effects of autism

- providing physical, emotional and educational support

- enhancing self-confidence and self-esteem through encouragement

- providing opportunities to enhance existing skills and interests

- providing a positive and respectful narrative about autism and the person.

It is about supporting people to develop existing interests and skills but also to experience new things and to engage in activities and relationships that are fulfilling for them. It is about working on the basis that people 'can do' if given the support to do so, but at the same time working sensitively and respectfully to ensure the experience is positive and not unpleasant, unduly anxiety provoking or aversive.

It is important that activities are meaningful and enjoyable. For example visiting a favourite store, museum or park will be better than a walk with no clear purpose, or baking a cake that gets to be eaten is preferable to baking for the sake of baking. There should always be a context that is relevant to the person.

Understanding and Responding to Autism: The SPELL framework (2nd edition)

Examples of good practice of positive approaches

Examples of good practice of positive approaches

- Formal, structured assessment of skills and interests. Listening to the person. This allows you to find the person's level of skill without too much trial and error.

- Persistent yet sensitive engagement – to increase level of confidence, self-esteem, interaction and motivation. Here the use of other person-centred approaches, such as active support, may be important. The supported rehearsal of difficult tasks and scenarios can help people to overcome fears and be more comfortable and flexible.

- Utilising special interests to aid motivation, for example, a special interest in trains and timetables – or codes or antiques may be used to help find a job.

- Small changes should be programmed – this is also important to help people become more flexible, learn new skills and access new and enjoyable activities.

- Intervene when behaviours are likely to reduce opportunity – it is important to deal with so-called challenging behaviour through holistic preventative approaches that respect individuality. For many people, implementing the SPELL framework and using active support or well-being approaches to help them achieve their goals will be important in doing this and may be enough. In some instances additional professional advice from doctors or psychologists might be necessary to investigate the causes and advise on intervention.

Examples of misunderstanding

- Someone being left to pursue activities of choice exclusively or without boundaries.

- A person avoids a new activity or an activity that is good for his or her physical, social or mental well-being.

Examples of violation

- Expectations are too low (for example, tasks are too easy or childish), which means the task is unlikely to be interesting for the individual and this results in boredom (which can result in self-stimulatory or challenging behaviour). No demands are made of the person.

- Expectations are too high (for example, tasks are too hard), which can lead to frustration/panic and then to challenging behaviour in the form of a meltdown or shutdown.

- Someone being referred to, or treated in, demeaning or insensitive terms.

- Environment contains negative imagery or is poorly maintained or appointed.

- Staff use inappropriate language when offering activities, which ignore the need to present choices in ways that are meaningful to the person. For example 'you don't want to go swimming do you?' rather than asking 'shall we go swimming or bowling?' or showing symbols of activities

- Staff using sarcasm or negative language that undermines self-esteem, for example pointing out things that the person has done wrong or making a joke out of things that the person has done well. One person with Asperger syndrome told us, 'No matter how much and how often I cleaned or tidied my flat, the comment from staff was always sarcastic such as "It must be Christmas" … but if it was in a mess for a couple of days, staff would point out everything that was wrong. This lowered my self-esteem a lot and it was hard to feel at home.'

Understanding and Responding to Autism: The SPELL framework (2nd edition)

Supporting a boy to take part in exercise; something that is good for him. Notice how the teacher is running along beside him, encouraging and helping him to keep going. Note that they are all dressed for the activity – this aids concentration and focus as well as making the activity real and socially valid. For this young man this was especially important as he would only do exercise if he was wearing his school PE kit – it was the cue that it was time to exercise.

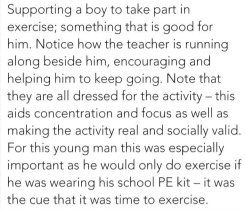

A young man feeding a horse – part of his work experience on the farm. This has positive benefits in several ways – he finds being with the animals calming and enjoyable and he is learning new skills that will help him get a job in the future.

Here a young lady is developing skills that may help her get a job in the future but in the meantime is engagement in something that is contributing to the experience of others – making sausage rolls for everyone's lunch. Notice how the member of staff is available to help but the lady is doing this part of the task independently but with encouragement.

Self-care skills are also important. Here Patrick is being helped to clean his teeth by himself.

This girl used to be afraid of dogs, to the extent that it stopped her going out. With a programme of very gentle exposure, using an older and very gentle dog, she is now much more comfortable with dogs and no longer afraid to go out of the house.

Someone being supported to do a new and exciting activity safely. Services are often very risk-averse and as those supporting people to live their lives, we should challenge this. In order to achieve a good quality of life, we have to take some risks. The aim here is to manage the risks so the activity is successful.

These boys are being supported to play snakes and ladders with a larger board, as dealing with small counters on a tiny board is frustrating. They are learning to take turns and to win and lose in a controlled situation with adult help when needed. There is also the element of rehearsal here as learning these skills will take more than one attempt. This is an example of a game for rehearsing important life skills

This boy is trying the obstacle course for the first time. It is something that is good for him to do and his teacher is helping him to be successful and encouraging him. This is a safe opportunity to try something uncomfortable or unknown.

Understanding and Responding to Autism: The SPELL framework (2nd edition)
© Pavilion Publishing and Media Ltd and its licensors 2018.

Here Patrick's mum is taking the opportunity to help Patrick learn his numbers while he is playing with his puzzle toy. The type of help she is providing is modelling or demonstration.

Patrick independently bringing in the post from the family mail box.

This is an example of good preparation to help someone to make their tea (spaghetti bolognaise). The staff in the service use active support to help people with autism be engaged and involved in all aspects of their lives. This preparation is also an example of structure – the ingredients are positioned in the order they will be used – this will reduce the need for verbal prompts during the activity.

Achieving positive approaches needs more than just understanding autism – it needs those supporting an individual on the autism spectrum to be able to facilitate engagement in meaningful activities including interactions. It needs those supporting individuals to be flexible and try new things and to learn from the experience; to work out what people like, need, want, feel and how they communicate and then to share this information with other people in their lives. **Annex 6** outlines some of the other approaches, such as person-centred active support, that can be useful in achieving positive approaches.

Watch the video **Patrick loading dishwasher** to see Patrick's mum supporting him and his brother to get involved in the things that are going on around the home. She is very skilful at providing just enough help to ensure success (see **Annex 6** for more information).

Watch the video **Social inclusion montage**. Not all the people in this montage are autistic but many of them are and you can see how people can be supported, according to their needs, preferences and interests to have meaningful interactions with others that build positive images and promote both inclusion and acceptance for autistic people (as well as many others with a disability).

Scenario 2

Mary has always loved watching show jumping on TV and loves looking at pictures of horses. Staff at the day centre start to explore the possibility of Mary trying riding. First, however, they have to see whether she actually likes horses 'in the flesh'. They arrange for her to go to local riding stables, initially to look at the horses from a distance. Mary seems keen to get closer so they arrange for someone to bring a horse close to the other side of a fence from where Mary is standing. Staff show her how to touch and stroke the horse's nose. Over a three-week period they visit the horses twice a week. It is clear that Mary loves the horses and having watched others riding, she emerges one day from the stable tack room with a riding hat on. Mary had her first riding lesson that week and continues to enjoy it. She is now supported to groom some of the horses and even does some mucking out.

Is this an example of good practice, misunderstanding or violation of the principle of positive approaches and expectations?

(Answers for this scenario are provided in **Annex 9**)

Empathy

In order to successfully support people and implement positive approaches it is essential to develop empathy for the individual. There are several aspects to this.

■ We need to develop an understanding of how the person thinks, communicates, learns and experiences the world. We do this through careful assessment based on contact with the individual and knowledge both of autism and of them. Interventions and strategies should reflect the individual's perspective as well as respect for them and their right to be different.

Understanding and Responding to Autism: The SPELL framework (2nd edition)
© Pavilion Publishing and Media Ltd and its licensors 2018.

- 'Go stand with them in the rain', said the late Donna Williams, an autistic woman who wrote several books giving personal insight into her autism. Listening to people (their words and their behaviour) can help us to understand how they see things that happen to them and how to help them.

- 'Being autistic, I have every right not to talk', said Tito Mukhopadhayay, a young autistic boy who was living and writing in India. He wrote a book, *Beyond the Silence,* when he was eight years old, which gives further insight into how autism affects him.

- We describe autistic people as lacking empathy but then we often expose them to conditions we might predict as problematic for them. It is really *our* lack of empathy for the autistic experience that is at fault as we merely project our own experiences, biases and prejudices onto the autistic person. This is particularly the case with sensory processing where we do not recognise the discomfort or distress of particular sensory sensations such as smell, touch or sound, as we do not feel it for ourselves. The consequence is that we may expose people to deeply problematic experiences in environments where we could have predicted problems. We therefore need to reflect on our own problems with empathy and work hard at getting in touch with how *this* child or *this* adult experiences the world.

 ## Examples of good practice of empathy

- Assess and record aversive events or stressors. Such events should be eliminated where possible and if not then sensitively and carefully managed. For example, if you know that someone finds dogs highly aversive then try to avoid situations where the person is going to be left in a room with a dog or even avoid a park where you know lots of people walk their dogs. However, being so afraid or anxious around dogs that it stops you ever going outside except in a car can have a serious impact on quality of life, therefore it is essential to try to sensitively and carefully help the person to become more tolerant of dogs. They don't have to get to the point of wanting one for a pet, just enough so that they can go out without being very afraid.

- Assess the person's sensory profile, for example sensitivities and level of registration. This might be through a formal assessment, such as a sensory profile assessment, or simply through the team having observed, recorded and shared information as they work with an individual. It would look not just at the individual directly but also at the environment, including the people around the individual.

- Use of devices (for example, headphones, smartphones or ear plugs) should be available when needed to screen out or reduce sound. This can help people concentrate as well as reducing levels of anxiety or arousal.

- Assess the person's level of comprehension; when teaching, frequently check what has been understood. Integrate opportunities to gently ask questions or ask someone to repeat back an instruction to make sure that you delivered it clearly. Often the level of comprehension of autistic people is misunderstood. We often hear the comment, 'Oh he understands everything I say', or, 'Well he speaks a lot so he must understand', without realising that the person might have difficulties in processing language or gestures or may be simply repeating what they have heard.

- Most importantly, develop a relationship of understanding with the person where you create opportunities for the person to communicate their likes and dislikes and things that worry them. Learning how to listen and learning about your own biases and misunderstandings and stereotyped or fixed views is very important.

- Information on assessing a sensory profile can be found in **Annex 7**.

Examples of misunderstanding

- Blanket attribution of 'autism' characteristics based on biased or outdated views.
- No application of individualised solutions or strategies.
- Person left to engage in preferred activity exclusively.

Examples of violation

- Person repeatedly confronted by aversive event or stressor.
- Assumptions made on the basis of vocabulary (level of ability); language capacity is over or under-estimated. (Vocabulary is rarely a good indicator of comprehension and does not take into account processing delays and literal understanding.)
- The worker 'personalises' their own experience or preference and projects onto the person. For example if they enjoy going to discos they assume everyone else will. If they are not distressed by a particular smell it does not occur that others might be. If they don't find a task difficult they assume others won't. If they are not interested in a particular topic, no one else will be and so on.

Understanding and Responding to Autism: The SPELL framework (2nd edition)

Some mainstream settings are highly problematic and aversive for autistic children and adults (such as busy environments as found in schools, supermarkets, train stations or airports) and some of the older, larger service settings involving large numbers of people were extremely problematic for autistic people.

Example: Joshua

Joshua is seven years old. He attends a mainstream school with a teaching assistant every afternoon. He has a special corner in the classroom in which he does most of his work. The teachers insist that he attends assembly and whole school events even though this makes him really anxious and over-stimulated. He spends the whole time with his hands over his ears and his face screwed up. He tries to escape but is brought back and made to sit on the floor with the other children in his class. This leaves him unable to concentrate on work for the rest of the day and he spends most of the time after this rocking and self-stimulating. The teachers say that he has to learn to cope in the 'real world', including crowded places, and they want him to be part of the school – he is supposed to be included after all.

One of the key things that we can do with regard to empathy is to take account of people's difficulty with language and with processing information. Therefore, reducing language or taking more time is one way to show empathy to autistic people.

Why is language so difficult? Essentially, it is a code – a code that requires knowledge and processing. Spoken words and sentences are auditory and abstract, whereas written words and sentences, and signs, symbols, objects and pictures are visual and concrete. By relying more heavily on visual methods of communication, you play to the strengths of autism and avoid some of the difficulties. Of course, people will differ but clarity of language and allowing time for processing is important for everyone to prevent misunderstanding.

Have you ever been somewhere new on holiday or with work? How do you navigate when on holiday in a foreign country? How do you communicate if you don't speak the language?

Thought also has to be given to visual methods of communication too. You can't just draw or print a pretty picture without considering what it would represent to someone with a literal understanding and rigidity of thought. Look at the following signs.

Which of these signs would leave you most confident that you were going into the right toilet? Which is the least ambiguous sign? What do you think would happen to an autistic person if they encountered one of the other types of symbols? For the next couple of weeks, look at the signs and symbols used in different places (restaurants, cafes, bars etc) and think about how autism friendly our society is and what we could do to make it more so.

Understanding and Responding to Autism: The SPELL framework (2nd edition)
© Pavilion Publishing and Media Ltd and its licensors 2018.

Which of these two pictures is the best representation of 'tractor'?

The second picture would generally be considered better as it is less ambiguous. The first could equally well refer to 'farmer'.

Most people would recognise this sign as indicating disability access. It is fairly unambiguous. However, it is important to remember that for autistic people, the literal understanding could be that they can't use the toilet with this sign on the door because they don't have a wheelchair.

Which of these signs would best symbolise a hot drink (tea or coffee etc)?

Again, the illustration of the cup and saucer is probably better as the photo has too many other things going on, which might be confusing.

These are examples of door signs. The one on the left clearly indicates the ICT room. The one on the right is a photo of the lounge/chill-out room. When you open the door, you see what is in the photo.

This is a dishwasher with drawers, which is much easier for someone in a wheelchair to fill. However, the main point here is that the photos on the front guide people to know what should be in each drawer and reduce the need for language.

When using photos to represent meals you have to be very careful. This is what ravioli might look in a restaurant but if you use this picture some autistic people might always expect it to look just like this, with mushrooms on the table, olive oil etc. If they have it out of a tin, then it won't look like this!

Similarly, showing people a tin of beans will probably not initially help them to understand that they are having beans for tea.

It can be better to take photos of the food the person actually eats and how they normally have it presented.

Most people recognise this as a symbol of a question or making a choice.

However we do sometimes have to teach people what symbols mean by repeatedly using it in conjunction with actions and situations.

Understanding and Responding to Autism: The SPELL framework (2nd edition)
© Pavilion Publishing and Media Ltd and its licensors 2018.

Most people will recognise this as the symbol of poison. However, some people (and not necessarily autistic people) would say this is the symbol for pirates.

When asked what this first picture symbolised, one person responded with 'chess pieces' – a rook, a bishop and a pawn! You need to find things that provide a good, unambiguous image of the object to be most helpful to people. Don't assume that what you see is what other people see. The second picture is more clearly a knife, fork and spoon for some but not others. It is important to think carefully about what images you use.

Some important points to remember

- Sensory processing differences are significant for autistic children and adults and they may process information more slowly. A literal understanding sometimes means autistic people don't see things in the same way as those who are not on the autism spectrum.

- Anxiety can be greatly reduced by attending to the physical and sensory environment.

- Physical and sensory environment includes staff, carers and other people. Those who work most closely with autistic people will have a high impact on the environment and a thoughtful approach is always needed to anticipate and plan. Skilled support involves knowing what to do (e.g. visual structure, calm approach) and what to avoid (e.g. over use of language, unplanned activity, perfumes etc).

- Some children and adults may be 'sensory seeking' (constantly finding stimulation, perhaps even through self-injury). Other people may appear to be avoiding sensory stimulation. Some people can be both.

- Within the so called 'sensory seeking' group of children or adults, a low registration of pain (high pain threshold) is particularly important in self-injury – people can do quite a lot of damage to themselves without even realising it. Paying attention to sensory needs will play a huge part in reducing anxiety and self-injurious behaviour.

Good communication support

It is perfectly natural for most of us to engage in conversations and interactions which are vague and where 'small talk' or chattiness is the norm. Many autistic people report such interactions as difficult and confusing – and pointless. We should be aware of the communication style of the people we are working with to get it right, and we should be careful not to ask open ended questions of people who find such questions difficult to respond to. 'Would you like to do this?' or, 'Are you interested in this?' are better questions than, 'What would you like to do? or, 'How are you?'

It isn't helpful to keep talking to people while they are engaged in an activity unless it is giving specific guidance on the task itself; it is a form of distraction and we should remember that too many verbal prompts may make the person over-reliant on these and unable to become more independent. It is possible to be warm and caring and use non-verbal communication while being direct.

Understanding and Responding to Autism: The SPELL framework (2nd edition)
© Pavilion Publishing and Media Ltd and its licensors 2018.

Therefore, good communication support should be:

- quiet
- direct – as few words as possible
- specific and clear as to what is expected
- accompanied by non-verbal cues where possible and appropriate for the individual
- accompanied by opportunities for choice.

It is possible that you might have to 'experiment' to find out what works and what doesn't for each individual, but that is part of the whole process. However, once you have found the best way to communicate for an individual, it is important that this plan is shared and used – this will help ensure a consistent approach is used.

By doing this you can often greatly reduce the need for challenging behaviour. If you give people a direct, and non-verbal, way of communicating (such as that they need to be alone or need to leave the situation they are in) they will be able to maintain control more easily and become less frustrated. Some examples of this include things like a card to hold up, a hand held up, turning away, one word to say (for example, 'out', 'help') etc. Sometimes the methods that people choose to communicate with may appear to be inappropriate, but a 15-year-old boy swearing at someone is probably relatively culturally and age-appropriate and substantially better than kicking, punching or biting!

Think about an individual you support – what ways do they use to communicate? Are there any times when you think they get frustrated and struggle to communicate? Are there any ways you could help them to better understand or communicate?

Scenario 3

Staff working with Joshua are convinced that he is over-sensitive to something in the environment but they don't know how to go about finding out what it is. They ask the local clinical psychologist for help but are told not to worry – it is 'just the autism' that is making him 'difficult' and they should just keep giving him his medication.

Is this an example of good practice, misunderstanding or violation of the principle of empathy?

(Answers for this scenario are provided in **Annex 9**)

See **Annex 6** for some resources on adapting and supporting communication.

Low arousal

The first thing to note about a low-arousal approach is that it is not the same as no arousal. It is not about leaving people alone with no stimulation or having a completely barren environment. It is not just about the environment, but also about interactions. It is particularly important that consideration is given to the specific sensory sensitivities experienced by the individual.

What sorts of things are difficult for you to cope with? It might be loud noises or being in crowds or particular smells. What do you do to cope with potentially aversive situations?

Most successful interventions for autistic people take place against a background of low arousal. A low-arousal approach involves:

- calm, focused, planned intervention and interactions
- awareness of environmental/sensory impact
- removal or reduction of aversive (unpleasant) or distracting stimuli
- improving discrimination concentration
- a non-confrontational style of interaction
- supportive rehearsal of the potentially aversive event.

In many services used by autistic children or adults, staff may be (usually unintentionally) a source of over-arousal. It is helpful to acquire habits to:

- speak softly and work quietly
- reduce the use of language and to rely more on visual methods of communication
- give simple direct instructions
- allow time for processing
- always be aware of the sensory environment (audit as you go)
- be aware of how the person's sensory needs will affect their programme of activity.

Understanding and Responding to Autism: The SPELL framework (2nd edition)
© Pavilion Publishing and Media Ltd and its licensors 2018.

Examples of good practice of a low-arousal approach

- Doing a daily audit of the environment to eliminate or reduce undesired stimuli, for example noise, heat, light, smell, touch, visual conditions, clutter etc.
- Assessing a sensory profile and recording it in the person's person-centred plan.
- Those supporting people speaking clearly and working calmly and quietly.
- Interactions are clear and unambiguous – language is reduced.

Obviously the application of the principle of low arousal has to be individualised. For some people noise might not be a problem but visual distraction is very powerful. If misinterpreted, a low-arousal approach can result in denial of stimulating or arousing experiences. Most people will need these experiences built into a programme of gradual exposure – a little at a time.

An example of helping people through supportive rehearsal of a potentially aversive event was seen earlier with the young lady who was supported to be able to be near dogs so that she could leave her house.

Another example would be helping someone to prepare to go to the dentist by very gradually exposing them to what is needed, for example the first step might just be to show the whole process visually and then attempting each part incrementally. The steps might be driving down the street where the dentist is located, then stopping outside, then going to the door, then saying hello to the receptionist, then just meeting the dentist, then sitting in the chair but having nothing done, up to the point that they feel they can let the dentist look at their teeth.

It has been found helpful to include a favourite activity as part of the process – for example going at a favourite shop after the visit to the dentist. Not as a reward but part of the sequence.

Some further examples of good practice would be reducing noise and clutter, keeping things that might cause a distraction out of sight, ensuring that powerful smells are eliminated, for example, strong smelling flowers, perfumes and air fresheners can all be difficult for autistic people (as well as for many in the general population).

Lighting is also very important. Natural light is preferred (although not too bright) and artificial light (especially fluorescent lighting) can cause great problems. Having an environment that has a variety of lighting options – from bright and natural to soft and subtle – can greatly help the individual and put them in control of their environment. Up-lighters (where light is projected onto ceilings) or hidden light bulbs, have been found by autistic people to be particularly helpful.

Some examples of what you might see happening in order to achieve a low-arousal approach are listed here:

- Reducing the amount of notices displayed on walls. Remember, if it goes on the wall it needs to go in a frame or on a notice board – the borders will help give structure.

- Having one room that is designated a quiet or low-arousal room, with comfy seats but no TV, limited pictures on the walls, low lighting etc.

- In schools, having wall displays that are well structured (see photos of display boards on p98 and p99).

- People should avoid wearing perfume or aftershave. Cigarette smells or air fresheners should be avoided.

- Strip florescent lighting should be replaced with other forms of adjustable light sources such as up-lighters.

- The temperature within a setting should be adjustable, with ways for people to keep cool on hot days. Activities should take into account the need for people to keep cool.

- Air filters should be fitted to windows as appropriate to prevent hay fever.

- Carpets (without loud and distracting patterns) should be used as these dampen noise and are seen as more homely and welcoming.

- Be aware that floral displays can be problematic. Flowers such as lilies can be very difficult for people with hay fever and those with a sensitivity to strong smells.

- Staff should wear clothes that are relatively neutral as the people they support may be sensitive to bright colours.

- Be aware that black print on white paper can be very difficult for children with additional learning difficulties such as dyslexia. Similarly, using fonts that are clear and easy to read is really important if students are to be able to process information. Fonts such as Verdana usually work well. Coloured paper will help. Advice from a speech and language therapist should be sought if specific difficulties are encountered.

Examples of misunderstanding

- Environment being 'spartan' or austere.
- Low-arousal approach being interpreted as 'no arousal'.
- Problem behaviours not being dealt with (interactions avoided).

Sometimes people hear 'low arousal' and think 'no arousal' – an environment that is low arousal for one person might seem spartan or austere to others but it doesn't have to be; it comes down to individual needs and preferences. Some people without autism like a minimalist approach that other people would find barren and cold. It is here that an understanding of the needs of others is important and that staff avoid projecting their own preferences.

Examples of violation

- Interactions are confrontational in nature, rather than positive and helpful. Confrontation might be in body language (for example, physical, as would be used in some physical intervention, or simply 'towering over' someone or standing too close to them, or talking too loudly or using negative language, such as, 'Don't walk on the grass' rather than 'Walk on the path').

- Environment maintains known stressors, for example:
  - loud or indiscriminate TV or music, maybe TV, radio and music from stereo on at the same time.
  - banging/squeaking doors
  - odours (including perfumes, air fresheners or highly perfumed flowers)
  - background noise (such as traffic on the roads or people talking)
  - harsh (especially fluorescent) lighting
  - distractions (such as lots of non-relevant materials in the workspace when someone is trying to concentrate on one particular task or staff talking about other things at the same time as supporting someone to engage in a task)
  - people fighting/disagreeing or staff being disrespectful to other staff in front of service users – many autistic people can pick up on a tense or strange atmosphere and can find this stressful and difficult.
- Staff not giving people time to respond; they might finish their sentences for them or try to guess what people are trying to say without listening to them and letting them finish.

It is important to remember that people might be sensitive to things that we are hardly even aware of; it might take some careful investigating to find out what it is they are sensitive to.

In the meantime those supporting people with autism should be very aware of the environment and their own style of interaction.

Example: Marie

Marie attends a mainstream school. Her teacher has recently attended SPELL training and has managed to introduce a low-arousal approach in conjunction with a visual timetable in the classroom, which the teacher is convinced is benefitting all the children, not just Marie. Marie's attention has improved immensely and the frequency with which she self-stimulates and gets anxious in class has dropped. However, when Marie is at assembly or in PE in the hall, she becomes extremely anxious and struggles to stay in the class line, or indeed in the hall. She will occasionally hit the child beside her and generally becomes very disruptive. Initially the teacher thought that it was the fact that there were so many children in the hall and that the main problem was the noise and the fact that she was expected to stay still. She persuaded the head teacher to allow her to take Marie out of assembly and to hold a small group assembly with some other children each week. Marie coped much better with this. The teacher then began to work on the PE

Understanding and Responding to Autism: The SPELL framework (2nd edition)
© Pavilion Publishing and Media Ltd and its licensors 2018.

sessions for Marie. She started to take Marie into the hall once a week with a small group of children for a short period of time. However, the moment Marie entered the hall she began to rock and appear unsettled. This became worse when the teacher started to talk and the other children started to run around or take part in games. Marie refused to take part, even though it was a game that during the summer months she had joined in with outside.

The teacher spent some time trying to work out what might be bothering Marie – eventually her hypothesis was that three things were happening. First, the walls of the hall were covered in art displays that were not very well structured or organised with lots of bright colours put together; Marie seemed to be avoiding these displays, standing in the one corner where there were no pictures on the wall. Second, she noticed that if she spoke very quietly and instructed the children to be silent that Marie seemed slightly better. If she held a written instruction above her head, Marie was more likely to join in. When she spoke loudly her voice echoed and Marie stopped responding and put her hands over her ears. Third, she noticed that the floor vibrated a lot when the children ran or jumped. When the children worked on mats or were instructed to tip toe very gently Marie was more likely to join in. The teacher arranged to visit a local special school for children with autism and sought advice on making autism-friendly displays. She then offered to redo the displays in the hall to structure them and reduce the arousal. She developed a PE programme that allowed Marie to join in at least some of each PE class, using games that required all the children to be quiet and to follow written instructions and physical demonstrations and that allowed children to work on mats for part of the time. When she needed to do things with the other kids that she knew Marie would find difficult, she arranged for the learning support assistant to work with Marie in a side room or out on the playground. The amount of time Marie spends in the whole class situation in the hall has increased and she now even attends some whole school assemblies but sits near the door so that if it gets too much she can leave. She doesn't usually need to leave – just knowing she can seems to help the anxiety.

Many of the photos used earlier for structured environment, positive approaches and empathy are also examples of a low-arousal approach. Some further examples are given overleaf.

Remember that what low arousal looks like might differ from individual to individual.

Some examples of a low-arousal approach (and some bad examples)

A visit to the aquarium might be a wonderful experience for some people, but for others the noise of other people or the noise of the tank mechanisms and the hundreds of fast-moving and multi-coloured fish might be a bit too much stimulation.

You have seen this picture before – the environment is tidy and although there are things on the benches there is space to work and most things are in the cupboards.

This is a bicycle workshop in Jersey – the environment is carefully structured and kept tidy – there is a shadow board for the tools and there is space to work. There is natural light.

This is an example of a display board in a school that is structured and therefore lower arousal than one might find in most mainstream schools. Having the background in one block of colour and the use of frames around the photos help to make each element distinct and therefore clearer. Avoiding overlapping images and too many different colours is very important.

Understanding and Responding to Autism: The SPELL framework (2nd edition)
© Pavilion Publishing and Media Ltd and its licensors 2018.

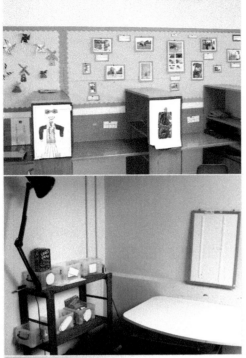

Another example of a display at a school for autistic children – you can also see the children's workstations which are generally low arousal apart from their visual timetables.

This is a workstation for an adult who requires a very low-arousal environment and use of structure to help him take part in leisure and educational activities. He only uses this environment to work in – he joins in with mealtimes and some social activities in a larger group.

For some autistic people, this might be the type of kitchen they require – with almost everything hidden behind sliding doors. Some people without autism may also like this type of minimalist decor. Everything that could be distracting or arousing is kept out of view.

Again, a very low-arousal environment – very minimalist. For some this would be too minimalist but for others this would be just right.

This is an entrance to a classroom for autistic children. Each child has a place for their coat, bag, shoes etc, denoted by a photo of the child with his/her name under it. The child comes to school in the morning and can put their coat and shoes away without help. The teachers introduce some flexibility by changing the locker allocation after a week or two (ie. by putting the children's photo on a different locker). The yellow line on the floor is to help children work out how to pass people who are standing at their own lockers.

This is from an institution where staff had tried to make the environment more 'child friendly'. Did it work?

In general we would say that this display would be very distracting – there are multiple colours used with letters overlapping and not distinct. The TV is placed in a position where there are windows either side and light is shining on the screen. This would make it very difficult for many people with autism (and indeed many people without autism) to watch the TV.

Thinking activity

These photos illustrated issues for sensitivity to environmental stimuli – thinking about the people that you know, identify other sensory sensitivities and what we might do to keep the environment low arousal?

Can you think of some examples of how interactions can be difficult for those on the autism spectrum?

Understanding and Responding to Autism: The SPELL framework (2nd edition)
© Pavilion Publishing and Media Ltd and its licensors 2018.

Scenario 4

When building the new hall at a school that had a unit providing support for 20 children on the autism spectrum, the head teacher insisted that it was essential to spend a little bit more money to use special bricks that had sound-proofing qualities to reduce the echo, lots of windows around the roof with blinds that could be used to adjust the level of light and a special floor that was quieter and 'softer' to run on.

Is this an example of good practice, misunderstanding or violation of the principle of low arousal?

(Answers for each scenario are provided in **Annex 9**)

Links

This final element of the framework is about two key things – ensuring consistency of approach for the individual and ensuring that their view is listened to. Autistic children and adults do not live in isolation but have a network of family members, acquaintances, professionals and others. They are often being supported by a team of staff (not just one person) and attending school or college, or they are employed. How the members of their network communicate and work together in partnership can be crucial in making smooth and comprehensible arrangements for the individual concerned. Links are also about helping the person to access, and be included in, mainstream activities in society, not just autism-specific activities (for example, NAS has specialist schools but these work with mainstream schools to help the children access activities and classes within the mainstream settings). Links are also about helping people to be able to access normal everyday activities in the community, like being able to use public transport, go to the shops and use the local swimming pool. It is about reasonable adjustments, accessibility and understanding the barriers.

Another important element is that the people themselves are actively involved in their own lives and are encouraged to be involved. Their views are listened to and they lead their plans and how they are supported.

Joanne Edgar (a parent of a autistic child) wrote in her 1999 book, *Love, Hope and Autism*: 'We went home and waited for the trail of professionals we felt sure would now beat a path to our door with endless bits of advice and practical things to that would help … they did not come.'

On the other hand, we often hear and read accounts of the experience of families who complain that they have had to deal with large numbers of different professionals, each of whom will do or say something different.

We also often find that even within teams supporting individuals on a day-to-day basis there can be differences between how one person supports an individual and how the next person does. The team members should not be making it up as they go along, but working to clear guidance and with a firm knowledge of what the individual needs and wants. They should not be imposing their beliefs or doing what they personally think they should do or want to do. Personalised planning, led by the autistic person, and a support profile/plan can be important tools here so that all members of the person's network share information necessary to support them in a consistent manner.

Examples of good practice

■ Maintaining effective communication between agencies and individuals, including written and verbal, and formal and informal communication.

■ Close collaboration between services or schools and families. The families are treated as experts on their child rather than their views and experiences being dismissed. Families inform the school when things have happened that might affect the child's day and the school shares what has happened during the day.

■ Families are involved in decisions that might affect the child or adult (unless the adult has specifically requested for the family not to be involved).

■ Regular opportunities and events for sharing views and information, such as team meetings in services and meetings with everyone who works with the person across services.

■ Ensuring a high level of consistency of approach, for example through planned intervention (rather than leaving what happens to an individual to chance), and ensuring everyone is working to an agreed plan/approach.

■ Taking a long-term perspective in lifestyle/person-centred planning involving the individual in every aspect. Some people who can easily advocate for themselves might not want a plan but the planning process can help people who require more support to have their views heard and their future considered. A good personalised plan, led wherever possible by the person themselves, will outline what is important to everyone. A good planning process is flexible in the methods and tools used. Making the goals and the documents as concrete as possible is important. Some people may not want a written plan but want the opportunity to discuss their goals and get the support they need to achieve them. An example of the main sections of a personalised plan for a man on the autism spectrum is provided in **Annex 8**.

Example: Lucy

Lucy is 18 and attends a special school for autistic children. For the past three years the school has been working with Lucy and her parents to plan for her transition to college and, ultimately, employment. She has strengths in maths and science and has been supported to attend maths and science GCSE lessons and then A-level classes at the mainstream secondary school. The rest of the time she attends lessons focusing on literacy and life skills. During the week she boards and gets involved in all the activities of daily life around the home. The school has worked with her parents to ensure that consistent support is provided for activities that might occur in both environments. She is also supported to attend a local dance school in the evening as she is a talented dancer and she takes part in local events with the other dancers. She was supported to work in a local nursery for work experience, where she taught the children some basic dance moves once a week. For the past year, her individualised education plan (IEP) meetings have developed into person-centred planning meetings and now involve both Lucy and the link person from the college that Lucy hopes to attend next year.

Examples of misunderstanding

- Uniformity mistaken for consistency.
- Reliance on formal systems of communication exclusively.
- Reliance on informal systems of communication exclusively.

Example: Samuel

Samuel lives in a residential service for people with intellectual disability and attends an activity centre. About five years ago an incident of destructive behaviour was put down to over-stimulation and resulted in a lot of activities being withdrawn from Samuel's programme at the centre. This was recorded in his notes and a letter sent back to the service.

On the basis of this letter the staff in the home also withdrew lots of stimulation from Samuel. Staff work on the basis that as long as they keep things the same in both environments with limited stimulation there will be no reoccurrence of the incident. However, they do not communicate with each other on a regular basis and the support in both environments continues to be based on the incident five years ago. Samuel has two person-centred plans – one developed by the day centre and one by the residential service.

Examples of violation

- Professionals ignore or act in isolation from parents and each other.
- Changes to a programme are undertaken arbitrarily without consultation.
- There are no life planning systems, or if they do exist they are only short-term.
- The person is being excluded from the planning process because they are seen as inhibiting or passive.
- Parent/carers are excluded from decision-making because their son/daughter is an adult.

Example: Brian

Brian likes to empty the dishwasher and this activity has become part of his daily routine. However, support staff report that sometimes he becomes quite aggressive when doing this activity. The service manager decided to observe the activity over a couple of days and discovered that support staff were not consistently supporting the activity. When Brian emptied the dishwasher in the morning, the member of staff with him encouraged him to put the small plate on the top rack rather than the bottom and when he put the cup in the wrong way up the member of staff just discreetly turned it round so that it would wash properly. In the evening when a different member of staff supported him he was told to put the small plates on the bottom rack and was corrected several times and made to turn the cups round himself. After the third cup, he turned and threw the cup in the sink.

Example: Jamie

Jamie requires a special diet to help to keep her weight down and to help control some food intolerances. The diet has been agreed between her parents and the specialist dietician. A copy of the diet is sent to the respite home and to the day centre.

Jamie usually takes a packed lunch to the day centre and during cookery sessions she is supported to make something nice from her list of allowed foods. At the respite centre, staff do not follow the diet most of the time as it usually requires that they prepare separate food for Jamie. They say that it is unfair that other people in the home should be allowed to eat the nice things and that Jamie can't. They say that Jamie is an adult and should be allowed to choose what she eats even if that isn't always what is best for her health.

Answers for each scenario are provided in **Annex 9**.

Film clips

Watch some of the video clips below (available from the online resources page) illustrating the SPELL framework in practice and see if you can pick out the different elements of the framework.

Watch the video **Home–school transition**: Andrew and Joshua have just come home to the hostel after school (they live in a small hostel provided by the school for at least part of the week). After a snack and a drink they go through the school day with staff (this is called 'recall') and then they go through the plan for the evening. Note how Joshua reads his communication book himself, whereas Andrew still needs the member of staff supporting him to read it. Andrew uses PECS to do his timetable, whereas Joshua uses a mixture of writing and symbols. The member of staff has a copy of Joshua's timetable already written out so that Joshua can look at it if needed, but they are encouraging him to do it himself as much as possible to improve his independence. This helps to reduce the risk that he will become frustrated. Joshua's writing is very big but the staff member doesn't try to make him write small or neatly as that is not the purpose of the activity – it is about helping Joshua to work out and write down what will happen in the evening to help reduce his anxiety and promote predictability while promoting independence at the same time.

Watch the video **Working at new ground**. This video shows a series of clips taken during the course of a day at New Ground gardening project. It starts with Gareth using visual structure to help him get started on his day from social tasks or activities, such as saying good morning, to making a cup of tea. There is then time to chat and to plan or recap on what has to be done. After that, people get down to work and engage in a variety of activities. Notice how the whiteboard is used both for staff and for individuals with autism spectrum conditions to provide a visual reminder. This is a socially valid and age-appropriate way of providing structure. On some tasks people can work relatively independently; on other tasks they need a little more support. This clip shows some good examples of person-centred active support as well as SPELL, especially where Gareth is being supported to cut open the bags to make liners for the hanging baskets. All of the people in this clip are familiar with the tasks they are doing and with the environment. It is clearly a work environment and, although some might say that the environment is a little cluttered, only the materials needed for the task of making the hanging baskets are in the environment and everything that is needed is to hand.

Remember…

- SPELL is a framework – a foundation on which to build other person-centred approaches and develop practice.

- By implementing the framework you can achieve a lot in terms of quality of life – increasing choice, independence, participation etc as well as reducing 'challenging behaviours'.

- However, it might not be the only course of action needed – you may need to deal with co-occurring conditions, and don't be afraid to ask for help.

It is also possible that you will need to involve external professionals to support the implementation of the framework. Working with a GP/paediatrician or psychiatrist will be important if there are medical or mental health issues – or a speech and language therapist over specific communication aspects. You may need a psychologist to do a functional assessment of people showing concerning behaviours.

You might need an occupational therapist for sensory processing assessments and interventions or a physiotherapist with exercise or activities. A dietician may also be helpful in dealing with allergies/intolerances. You might also need to access a specialist ADHD clinic if the child or adult you support also has ADHD.

Conclusions

The SPELL framework was initially developed as a means of understanding and responding to the needs of the autistic population of the National Autistic Society. As such it was more aligned with the needs of those individuals described as more 'classically' or 'severely' autistic. Over the years it has changed to accommodate those individuals described as 'more able' or with Asperger syndrome, and despite some differences in detail we believe the approach also serves the needs of these individuals, as it has a socially valid basis. It is based on what everyone needs in order to have a good quality of life:

- We all need structure in our lives.

- We all need to be seen positively, and valued and allowed to pursue our interests and develop our strengths.

- We all need other people to have empathy for our point of view and us for theirs.

- We all need to reduce unhealthy stress and confrontation in our lives.

- We all need to be treated fairly and consistently.

Understanding and Responding to Autism: The SPELL framework (2nd edition)
© Pavilion Publishing and Media Ltd and its licensors 2018.

The SPELL framework therefore attempts to understand and respond to the unique needs of the autistic individual by applying holistic principles of what is understood to be best practice.

It is the foundation or essential companion for all other interventions or approaches and it creates an autism-friendly environment. It is generally accepted that if it is friendly to autism it is friendly to everyone.

References
and further reading

Allen D, James W, Evans J, Hawkins S & Jenkins R (2005) Positive behavioural support: definition, current status and future directions. *Tizard Learning Disability Review* **10** (2) 4–11.

Asperger H (1944) Die autistischen psychopathen im kindesalter. *Archiv fur Psychiatrie und Nervenkrankheiten* **117** 76–136.

Attwood T (2007) *The Complete Guide to Asperger Syndrome*. London: Jessica Kingsley Publishers.

Baieli S, Pavone L, Meli C, Fiumara A & Coleman M (2003) Autism and phenylketonuria. *Journal of Autism and Developmental Disorders* **33** (2) 201–204.

Baird, G, Simonoff E, Pickles A, Chandler S, Loucas T, Meldrum D & Charman T (2006) Prevalence of disorders of the autism spectrum in a population cohort of children in South Thames: the Special Needs and Autism Project (SNAP). *The Lancet* **368** (9531) 210–215.

Baron-Cohen S (2008) *Autism and Asperger Syndrome: The facts.* Oxford: Oxford University Press.

Baron-Cohen S, Leslie, A & Frith, U (1985) Does the autistic child have a "theory of mind"? *Cognition* **21** (1) 37–46.

Baron-Cohen S, Wheelwright S, Stott C, Bolton P & Goodyer I (1997) Is there a link between engineering and autism? *Autism* **1** 153–163.

Baird G, Simonoff E, Pickles A, Chandler S, Loucas T, Meldrum D & Charman T (2006) Prevalence of disorders of the autism spectrum in a population cohort of children in South Thames: the Special Needs and Autism Project (SNAP). *The Lancet* **368** (9531) 210–215.

Beggiato A, Peyre H, Maruani A, Scheid I, Rastam M, Amsellem F, Gillberg CI, Leboyer M, Bourgeron T, Gillberg C & Delorme R (2017) Gender differences in autism spectrum disorders: Divergence among specific core symptoms. *Autism Research* **10**: 680–689.

Bettleheim B (1967) *The Empty Fortress: Infantile autism and the birth of the self.* New York: The Free Press.

Bodner-Johnson B (1996) Total communication: a professional point of view. In: S Schwartz (Ed) *Choices in Deafness.* Bethesda: Woodbine House.

Bondy AS & Frost L (2001) The picture exchange communication system. *Behavior Modification* **25** (5) 725–744.

Bondy AS & Frost LA (1994) The picture exchange communication system. *Focus on Autism and Other Developmental Disabilities* **9** (3) 1–19.

Brugha T, McManus S, Meltzer H, Smith J, Scott FJ, Purdon S, Harris J & Bankart J (2009) *Autism Spectrum Disorders in Adults Living in Households Throughout England: Report from the Adult Psychiatric Morbidity Survey 2007.* London: NHS Information Centre for Health and Social Care.

Burd L & Kerbeshian J (1985) Hyperlexia and a variant of hypergraphia. *Perceptual and Motor Skills* **60** 940–942.

Carr E, Horner, Turnbull AP, Marquis JG, Magito McLaughlin D, McAtee ML, Smith CE, Anderson Ryan K, Ruef MB & Doolabh A (1999) *Positive Behaviour Support for People with Developmental Disabilities: A research synthesis.* Washington: American Association on Mental Retardation.

Carr JH & Collins S (1992) *Working Towards Independence: A practical guide to teaching people with learning disabilities*. London: Jessica Kingsley Publishers.

Chakrabarti S & Fombonne E (2001) Pervasive developmental disorders in preschool children. *The Journal of the American Medical Association* **285** (24) 3093–3099.

Chess S (1977) Follow-up report on autism in congenital rubella. *Journal of Autism and Child Schizophrenia* **7** (1) 69–81.

Conti-Ramsden GM, Simkin Z & Botting NF (2006) The prevalence of autistic spectrum disorders in adolescents with a history of specific language impairment (SLI). *Journal of Child Psychology and Psychiatry* **47** (6) 621–628.

Dunn W (1999) *Sensory Profile Manual*. San Antonio, TX: Psychological Corporation.

Ecker C, Marquand A, Mourão-Miranda J, Johnston J, Daly E, Brammer MJ, Maltezos S, Murphy CM, Robertson D, Williams S & Murphy DGM (2010) Describing the brain in autism in five dimensions – magnetic resonance imaging-assisted diagnosis of autism spectrum disorder using a multiparameter classification approach. *The Journal of Neuroscience* **30** 10612–10623.

Edgar J (1999) *Love, Hope and Autism*. London: The National Autistic Society.

Ehlers S & Gillberg C (1993) The epidemiology of Asperger syndrome. A total population study. *Journal of Child Psychology* **34** 1327–1350.

Folstein S & Rutter M (1977) Infantile autism: a genetic study of 21 twin pairs. *Journal of Child Psychology and Psychiatry* **18** (4) 297–321.

Fombonne E (1999) The epidemiology of autism: a review. *Psychological Medicine* **29** 769–786.

Fombonne E (2005) The changing epidemiology of autism. *Journal of Applied Research in Intellectual Disabilities* **18** (4) 281–304.

Frith U (1991) Autism and Asperger Syndrome. Cambridge: Cambridge University Press. (Translation of Asperger's 1944 article.)

Frith U (2003) *Autism: Explaining the enigma* (2nd edition). Oxford: Basil Blackwell.

Frith U (2008) *Autism: A very short introduction*. Oxford: Oxford University Press.

Gabriels R & Hill D (Eds) (2002) *Autism: From research to individualized practice*. London: Jessica Kingsley Publishers.

Ghaziuddin E, Weidmer-Mikhail E & Ghaziuddin N (1998) Comorbidity of Asperger syndrome: a preliminary report. *Journal of Intellectual Disability Research* **42** (4) 279–283.

Gillberg C (2010) The ESSENCE in child psychiatry: Early Symptomatic Syndromes Eliciting Neurodevelopmental Clinical Examinations. *Research in Developmental Disabilities* **31** (6):1543–1551.

Gillberg C & Billstedt E (2000) Autism and Asperger syndrome: coexistence with other clinical disorders. *Acta Psychiatria Scandinavica* **102** 321–330.

Gillberg C, Gillberg IC, Rasmussen P, Kadesjö B, Söderström H, Råstam M, Johnson M, Rothenberger A & Niklasson L (2004) Co–existing disorders in ADHD – implications for diagnosis and intervention. *European Child and Adolescent Psychiatry* **13** 80–92.

Gillberg C, Grufman M, Persson E & Themner U (1986) Psychiatric disorders in mildly and severely mentally retarded urban children and adolescents: epidemiological aspects. *British Journal of Psychiatry* **149** 68–74.

Gore N, McGill P, Toogood S, Allen D, Hughes JC, Baker P, Hastings R, Noone S & Denne L (2013). Definition and scope for positive behaviour support. *International Journal of Positive Behavioural Support* **3** (2) 14–23.

Grandin T & Scariano M (1986) *Emergence: Labeled autistic*. Clayton Vic: Warner books.

Green H, McGinnity A, Meltzer H, Ford T & Goodman R (2005) *Mental Health of Children and Young People in Great Britain, 2004*. Basingstoke: Palgrave Macmillan.

Gerland G (1997) *Finding Out About Asperger Syndrome, High-functioning Autism and PDD*. London: Jessica Kingsley Publishers.

Hobson P (1995) *Autism and the Development of the Mind*. Hove: Psychology Press.

Howlin P (2003) Autistic spectrum disorders. *Psychiatry* **2** (8).

Howlin P (1997) *Autism: Preparing for adulthood*. London: Routledge.

Hughes JR & Melyn M (2005) EEG and seizures in autistic children and adolescents: further findings with therapeutic implications. *Clinical Neuroscience* **36** 15–20.

Jones J (2000) A total communication approach towards meeting the communication needs of people with learning disabilities. *Tizard Learning Disability Review* **5** (1) 20–26.

Jordan R & Jones G (1999) Review of research into educational interventions for children with autism in UK. *Autism* **3** 101–110.

Kanner L (1943) Autistic disturbances of affective contact. *Nervous Child* **2** 217–250.

Kantzer A-K, Fernell E, Westerlund J, Hagberg B, Gillberg C, Miniscalco C (2018) Young children who screen positive for autism: Stability, change and "comorbidity" over two years. *Research in Developmental Disabilities* **72** 297-307

Kenny L, Hattersley C, Molins B, Buckley C, Povey C & Pellicano E (2016) Which terms should be used to describe autism? Perspectives from the UK autism community. *Autism* **20** (4) 442 – 462.

Kern JK, Trivedi MH, Garver CR, Grannemann BD, Andrews AA, Savla JS, Johnson DG, Mehta JA & Schroeder JL (2006) The pattern of sensory processing abnormalities in autism. *Autism* **10** 480–494.

Kierkegaard S (1998) *The Point of View: Kierkegaard's writings, Vol 22*. New Jersey: Princeton University Press.

Kim JA, Szatmari P, Bryson SE, Streiner DL & Wilson FJ (2000) The prevalence of anxiety and mood problems among children with autism and Asperger syndrome. *Autism* **4** (2) 117–132.

Koegel LK, Koegel RL & Dunlap G (1996) *Positive Behavioral Support: Including people with difficult behavior in the community*. Baltimore: Brookes.

Kutscher ML (2005) *Kids in the Syndrome Mix of ADHD, LD, Asperger, Tourette's, Bipolar, and More! The one stop guide for parents, teachers, and other professionals*. London: Jessica Kingsley Publishers.

LaMalfa G, Lassi G, Bertelli M, Salvini R & Placidi GF (2004) Autism and intellectual disability: a study of prevalence on a sample of the Italian population. *Journal of Intellectual Disability Research* **48** 262–267.

LaVigna GW & Willis TJ (1995) Challenging behavior: a model for breaking the barriers to social and community integration. *Positive Practices* **1** (1) 8–15.

Leekam S, Nieto C, Libby S, Wing L & Gould J (2007) Describing the sensory abnormalities of children and adults with autism. *Journal of Autism and Developmental Disorders* **37** (5) 894–910.

Lotter V (1966) Epidemiology of autistic conditions in young children: prevalence. *Social Psychiatry* **1** 124–137.

Mansell J & J Beadle-Brown (2004) Person-centred planning or person-centred action? Policy and practice in intellectual disability services. *Journal of Applied Research in Intellectual Disabilities* **17** 1–9.

Mansell J & J Beadle-Brown (2012) *Active Support: Enabling and Empowering people with intellectual disabilities*. London: Jessica Kingsley Publishers.

Mansell J, Beadle-Brown J, Ashman B & Ockendon J (2005) *Person-centred Active Support: A multi-media training resource for staff to enable participation, inclusion and choice for people with learning disabilities*. Brighton: Pavilion Publishing.

Marcus LM, Lansing M, Andrews CE & Schopler E (1978) Improvement of teaching effectiveness in parents of autistic children. *Journal of the American Academy of Child Psychiatry* **17** (4) 625–639.

Marvin C (1998) Teaching and learning for children with profound and multiple learning difficulties. In: P Lacey & C Ouvry (Eds) *People with Profound and Multiple Learning Disabilities: A collaborative approach to meeting complex needs*. London: David Fulton

Matson J & Shoemaker M (2009) Intellectual disability and its relationship to autism spectrum disorders. *Research in Developmental Disabilities* **30** (6) 1107–1114.

Mesibov GB (1997) Formal and informal measures of the effectiveness of the TEACCH programme. *Autism* **1** 25–35.

Mukhopadhyay T (2000) *Beyond the Silence: My life, the world and autism*. London: National Autistic Society.

Muris P, Steerneman P, Merckelbach H, Holdrinet I & Meesters C (1998) Comorbid anxiety symptoms in children with pervasive developmental disorders. *Journal of Anxiety Disorders* **12** 387–393.

O'Brien CL & O'Brien J (2000) The origins of person-centered planning – a community of practice perspective. In: S Holburn & P Vietze (2002) *Person-centered Planning: Research, practice and future directions*. Baltimore: Brookes.

O'Brien G & Pearson J (2004) Autism and learning disability. *Autism* **8** (2) 125–140.

Ozonoff S & Cathcart K (1998) Effectiveness of home program intervention for young children with autism. *Journal of Autism and Developmental Disorders* **28** 25–32.

Panerai S, Fernante L, Caputo V & Impellizeri C (1998) Use of structured teaching for treatment of children with autism and severe profound mental retardation. *Education and Training in Mental Retardation and Developmental Disabilities* **33** 367–374.

Panerai S, Ferrante, L & Zingale M (2002) Benefits of the treatment and education of autistic and communication handicapped children (TEACCH) programme as compared with a non-specific approach. *Journal of Intellectual Disability Research* **46** 318–327.

Person B (2000) Brief report: a longitudinal study of quality of life and independence among adult men with autism. *Journal of Autism and Developmental Disorders* **30** 61–66.

Premack DG & Woodruff G (1978) Does the chimpanzee have a theory of mind? *Behavioral and Brain Sciences* **1** 515–526.

Rogers SJ & Pennington BF (1991) *A theoretical approach to the deficits in infantile autism. Development and Psychopathology* **3** 137–162.

Rogers SJ & Williams JHG (Eds) (2006) *Imitation and the Social Mind: In autism and typical development*. New York: Guildford Press.

Rutter M & Bartak L (1973) Special education treatment of autistic children: a comparative study 2: follow-up findings and implications for services. *Journal of Child Psychology and Psychiatry* **14** 241–270.

Sanderson H (2000) *Person-Centred Planning: Key features and approaches*. Valuing People Support Team website: www.valuingpeople.gov.uk.

Sapieras P & Beadle-Brown J (2006) The Effectiveness of TEACCH approach Programme for People with Autism in Greece. *Autism* **10** (4) 330–343.

Schopler E, Mesibov GB & Hearsey K (1995) Structured teaching in the TEACCH system. In: E Schopler & GB Mesibov (Eds) *Learning and Cognition in Autism*. New York: Plenum Press.

Understanding and Responding to Autism: The SPELL framework (2nd edition)
© Pavilion Publishing and Media Ltd and its licensors 2018.

Schopler E, Mesibov GB, DeVellis RF & Short A (1981) Treatment outcome for autistic children and their families. In: P Mittler (Ed) *Frontiers of Knowledge in Mental Retardation: Social, educational and behavioral aspects*. Baltimore: University Park.

Selikowitz M (2004) *ADHD: The facts*. Oxford: Oxford University Press.

Shore S (2003) *Beyond the Walls: Personal experiences with autism and Asperger syndrome*. Overland Park: Autism Asperger Publishing Company.

Siaperas P & Beadle-Brown J (2006) The effectiveness of the TEACCH approach programme for people with autism in Greece. *Autism* **10** (4) 330–343.

Simone R (2010) *Asperger's On the Job: Must-have advice for people with Asperger's or high functioning autism and their employers, educators and advocates*. Arlington, USA: Future Horizons.

Spratt EG, Nicholas JS, Brady KT, Carpenter LA, Hatcher CR, Meekins KA, Furlanetto RW, Charles JM (2012) Enhanced cortisol response to stress in children in autism. *Journal of Autism and Developmental Disorders* **42** (1) 75–81.

Tantam D (1991) Asperger syndrome in adulthood. In: U Frith (Ed) Autism and Asperger Syndrome. Cambridge: Cambridge University Press.

Tantam D & Prestwood S (1999) *A Mind of One's Own: A guide to the special difficulties and needs of the more able person with autism or Asperger syndrome* (3rd edition). London: The National Autistic Society.

Tomchek SD & Dunn W (2007) Sensory processing in children with and without autism: a comparative study using the short sensory profile. *American Journal of Occupational Therapy* **61** 190–200.

Tuchman R & Rapin I (2002) Epilepsy in autism. *The Lancet Neurology* **1** 352–358.

Tuchman R, Cuccaro M & Alessandri M (2010) Autism and epilepsy: historical perspective. *Brain and Development* **32** (9) 709–718.

Tutt R, Powell S & Thornton M (2006) Educational approaches in autism: what we know about what we do. *Educational Psychology in Practice* **22** (1) 69–81.

Vermeulen P (2001) *Autistic Thinking – This is the title*. London: Jessica Kingsley Publishers.

Vermeulen P (2012) *Autism as Context Blindness*. Kansas, USA: AAPC Publishing.

Wing L (1981) Asperger's syndrome: a clinical account. *Psychological Medicine* **11** 115–130.

Wing L (1996) *The Autistic Spectrum: A guide for parents and professionals*. London: Robinson Publishing.

Wing L & Gould J (1979) Severe impairments of social interaction and associated abnormalities in children: epidemiology and classification. *Journal of Autism and Developmental Disorders* **9** 11–29.

Wing L & Potter D (2002) The epidemiology of autistic spectrum disorders: is the prevalence rising? *Mental Retardation and Developmental Disabilities Research Review* **8** (3) 151–161.

World Health Organisation (1992) *International Statistical Classification of Diseases (2nd edition)*. London: WHO.

Yeargin-Allsopp M, Rice C, Karapurkar T, Doernberg N, Boyle C & Murphy C (2003) Prevalence of autism in a US metropolitan area. *Journal of the American Medical Association* **289** (1) 49.

Websites and other resources

Autism Research Centre, University of Cambridge: www.autismresearchcentre.com

Research Autism: www.researchautism.net

Steven Shore's website: www.autismasperger.net

The National Autistic Society: www.autism.org.uk

The Tizard Centre's website: www.kent.ac.uk/tizard (information on further study related to Autism)

Christopher Gillberg's webpage at University of Gothenburg (useful source of relevant research): https://www.gu.se/english/about_the_university/staff/?selectedTab=2&userId=xgilch&languageId =100001&siteNodeId=587114&contentId=-1&originalRequestURI=/english/about_the_university/ staff/&publicationsPerPage=500

Autism Society of America: www.autism-society.org

Temple Grandin's website: http://www.templegrandin.com

Website set up by Rudy Simone Aspergirl Society – this page talks about the female traits. http:// aspergirlsociety.org/female-as-traits/

Other relevant resources from Pavilion

Person-centred Active Support Training Pack (2nd Edition)

A training resource to enable participation, independence and choice for adults and children with intellectual and developmental disabilities

Julie Beadle-Brown, Bev Murphy and Jill Bradshaw

This new training resource reflects the changes in the social care and learning disability context in the UK as well as in many other countries, and the valuable experience the authors have gained from 13 years of using the resources for training in many different settings. This resource is designed for those who wish to lead face-to-face group-based training, which is still the recommended option for delivering training in person-centred active support to support teams. A copy of the accompanying self-study guide is included.

Person-centred Active Support Self-study Guide (2nd edition)

A self-study resource to enable participation, independence and choice for adults and children with intellectual and developmental disabilities

Julie Beadle-Brown, Bev Murphy and Jill Bradshaw

This book is designed to provide the learner with knowledge about what active support is, why it is important, what it looks like in practice, and some of the key facts around what is needed for success. It can be followed as self-study or as part of a training programme. It includes videos and exercises to promote independent thinking and learning. It is available in hard copy and digital formats and provides about 5 to 7 hours of learning, with a certificate of completion.

A Mismatch of Salience: Explorations of the nature of autism from theory to practice

By Damian Milton

A Mismatch of Salience brings together a range of Damian Milton's writings that span more than a decade. The book explores the communication and understanding difficulties that can create barriers between people on the autism spectrum and neurotypical people. It celebrates diversity in communication styles and human experience by re framing the view that autistic people represent a 'disordered other' not as an impairment, but a two-way mismatch of salience. It also looks at how our current knowledge has been created by non-autistic people on the 'outside', looking in. *A Mismatch of Salience* attempts to redress this balance.

Available at: https://www.pavpub.com/a-mismatch-of-salience/

The Anger Box: Sensory turmoil and pain in autism

By Phoebe Caldwell

Shifting attention away from presentation and symptoms of autism alone, Phoebe explores and attempts to understand the sensory issues experienced by those on the autistic spectrum and their neurobiological roots in an effort to find new ways of alleviating the distress that can characterise people on the autistic spectrum.

Available at: https://www.pavpub.com/the-anger-box/

Hall of Mirrors - Shards of Clarity: Autism, neuroscience and finding a sense of self

By Phoebe Caldwell

Drawing on Phoebe Caldwell's 40 years of experience and expert knowledge of autism and Intensive Interaction, *Hall of Mirrors – Shards of Clarity* marries recent neuroscience research evidence and practical approaches used in care to cover a wide range of vital subjects. Sense of self, confirmation, sensory issues, case studies and neuroscience findings are explored and weaved together in an inspired way which brings aims to bring theory into practice and vice versa, while at the same time listening to the voices of people with autism. The result is to allow everyone in the autism field to take a few steps forward with how they interact and support autistic people.

Available at: https://www.pavpub.com/hall-of-mirrors/

Autism and Intellectual Disability in Adults Volume 1 & 2

Edited by Damian Milton & Nicola Martin

Autism and Intellectual Disability in Adults: Volumes 1 & 2 explore issues and practice affecting the support of adults with intellectual disabilities who are on the autism spectrum. This volumes explore potential key moments in the lives of adults with intellectual disabilities who are on the autism spectrum, covering a breadth of subjects including; policy, health, economics, wellbeing and equality, as well as a wealth of practical information and advocacy-related material. The focus of this series is not on the causes of autism; our interest instead lies in considering ways in which autistic people (focusing here on those with additional intellectual impairments) can have the best possible quality of life, on their own terms. Common themes emerge between authors, including the fundamental requirement to acknowledge, respect and facilitate autistic expertise as being central to the production of research, policy and practice.

Available at: https://www.pavpub.com/autism-and-intellectual-disability-in-adults-volume-1/ and https://www.pavpub.com/autism-and-intellectual-disability-volume-2/

10 Rules for Ensuring People with Learning Disabilities and those who are on the Autism Spectrum Develop 'Challenging Behaviour' ...And maybe what we can do about it

By Damian Milton, Richard Mills and Simon Jones

Written in the voice of someone with autism, this pocket sized booklet directly addresses the many practices and assumptions that that cause so many problems for children and adults with autism and learning difficulties and their family, friends and carers.

Available at: https://www.pavpub.com/10-rules-for-challenging-behaviour/

Understanding Autism: A training pack for support staff and professionals based on 'Postcards from Aspie World'

By Dan Redfearn, Holly Turton, Helen Larder and Hayden Larder

This unique training pack is based on the premise that learning from the experience of someone on the autism spectrum can help those who support individuals to understand and to adapt their approach and therefore achieve better outcomes. Each pack comes with a set of postcards created by a young woman with Asperger's syndrome. The postcards are also available to buy separately and are a valuable resource to prompt and aid discussion.

Available at: https://www.pavpub.com/understanding-autism/

Choosing Autism Interventions: A research-based guide

By Bernard Fleming, Elisabeth Hurley and The Goth

This best-selling book provides an accessible evidence-based overview of the most commonly used interventions for children and adults on the autism spectrum. It summarises best clinical practice from the National Institute for Health and Care Excellence (NICE) and gives a set of tools to help you evaluate interventions for yourself. It is the first guide of its kind to meet the requirements of the NHS Information Standard.

Available at: https://www.pavpub.com/choosing-autism-interventions/

Autism Spectrum Conditions: A guide

by Eddie Chaplin, Steve Hardy and Lisa Underwood

Published in association with the Estia Centre, this guide provides a comprehensive introduction to working with people who have autism spectrum conditions.

Available at: https://www.pavpub.com/autism-spectrum-conditions/

Understanding and Supporting Children and Adults on the Autism Spectrum

by Julie Beadle-Brown and Richard Mills

This unique multi-media training and learning resource, informed by both research and practice, is written by experts and designed not only to help people understand autism spectrum conditions but also to give them a person-centred framework of intervention and support for children or adults on the autism spectrum.

Available at: https://www.pavpub.com/understanding-and-supporting-children-andadults-on-the-autism-spectrum/

BV - #0039 - 140421 - C40 - 246/186/8 - PB - 9781912755196 - Gloss Lamination